Test Your Pronunciation

Michael Vaughan-Rees

PENGUIN ENGLISH

Pearson Education Limited
Edinburgh Gate
Harlow
Essex CM20 2JE, England
and Associated Companies throughout the world.

ISBN 0 582 46904 X

This edition published 2002
Text copyright © Michael Vaughan-Rees 2002
Fourth impression, 2004

Designed and typeset by Pantek Arts Ltd, Maidstone, Kent
Test Your format devised by Peter Watcyn-Jones
Illustrations by Roger Fereday and Sarah Whimperis
Printed in China   EPC/03

Acknowledgements
It would be impossible to write 60 totally original pronunciation tests, and there are a number of people whose ideas I am aware of having borrowed directly. These include Brita Haycraft (the use of names for distinguishing individual sounds); Jonathan Marks (Test 54, *Sounds maze* and Test 38, *Correcting mistakes 2 Two-part correction*); Barbara Bradford, Judy Gilbert, Bryan Jenner and Joanne Kenworthy (contrastive stress, highlighting and intonation); Barbara Seidlhofer and her colleagues in Vienna (phonological 'chunks'). To these (as well as to others, including Adam Brown, David Crystal, Jennifer Jenkins, Camilla Dixo Lieff, Peter Roach, Paul Tench and John Wells) I would like to express my thanks and appreciation.

Michael Vaughan-Rees

The publishers make grateful acknowledgement to Curtis Brown on behalf of Jane Waller for permission to reproduce the extract on page 56 from Saving the *Dinosaurs* copyright ©6 Jane Waller, Piper/Pan Macmillan, 1994.

Published by Pearson Education Limited in association with Penguin Books Ltd, both companies being subsidiaries of Pearson plc.

For a complete list of the titles available from Penguin English please visit our website at www.penguinenglish.com, or write to your local Pearson Education office or to: Penguin English Marketing Department, Pearson Education, Edinburgh Gate, Harlow, Essex, CM20 2JE.

Contents

To the student

If you want to improve your pronunciation and to understand native English-speakers more easily, you will find the tests in this book very helpful.

The book tests eight main pronunciation areas:

1 **identifying vowels and consonants** (tests 1, 2, 4–6, 8, 19, 23–25, 31–34)
2 **connecting sounds with spelling, including rhymes** (tests 8, 23–28, 30–34, 39, 53, 57)
3 **word and phrase stress** (tests 7, 9, 10, 21, 29, 40, 41, 43)
4 **sentence stress and intonation** (tests 12–14, 18, 20, 22, 37, 38, 42, 50–52, 58, 59)
5 **identifying weak and strong forms of vowels** (tests 3, 11, 18)
6 **normal, fast speech** (tests 15–17, 46–49, 60)
7 **using and understanding phonemic script** (tests 35, 36, 54–56, 60)
8 **pronouncing numbers and expressions with numbers** (tests 44, 45)

Before deciding which areas are most useful for you, decide what your aim is. Do you simply want people to understand you better? Or do you want to sound as much like a native speaker as possible?

All language students will need to work on areas 1 and 2, because these are the building blocks of all spoken language. Listen out particularly for how vowel sounds may differ in **length** as well as **quality**. If you want to improve your writing as well as listening, the tests listed in area 2 will help. They show that there are, in fact, rules governing the relationship between **sounds** and **spelling**. If you have problems with area 3, you will find it difficult to make yourself understood by native speakers of English, and working on these tests will help you communicate.

Within area 4, concentrate at first on the tests up to Test 50; you may find 51, 52, 58 and 59 more difficult, but these will help you sound more like a native speaker. If this is your aim, or if you need to understand fast speech, then try the tests listed in areas 5 and 6. Area 7 will help you work out the pronunciation of words when you look them up in a dictionary. Area 8 will help you wherever you meet numbers, and in your professional use of English.

You can check your answers in the Answers section at the back of the book. Many of the tests also have tips with information and ideas to help you improve your performance. Don't forget to read these tips: they contain a lot of useful information.

When using this book, don't feel that you always have to have it open in front of you. You could try just listening to the CD, maybe with your eyes closed. The more you listen, the more the sounds, stress patterns and intonation of English will become familiar to you. And the easier the tests will become.

Note: Some tests in this book (especially the ones called *Odd one out* and *Grouping rhyming words*) include unusual vocabulary that will not be familiar to you. You don't need to know the meaning of these words to complete the test, and can always look them up in a dictionary afterwards.

Michael Vaughan-Rees

Explanation of terms

Vowels and consonants
The terms are used both for writing and speech. You will usually find a term such as **vowel sound** or **written vowel** when you need to know the difference.

Phonemes and phonemic script
Individual vowel or consonant sounds are called **phonemes**. In phonemic script (often called **phonemic symbols** or **notation**), each symbol stands for a single phoneme. (In Test 4 'Peter' is written /piːtə/, for example.)

Word stress
Spoken words consist of one or more **syllables**. In two-syllable words one syllable is **stressed**, the other **weak**. Longer words such as 'economic' may have three degrees of stress: in this case, **primary** stress on the third syllable; **secondary** stress on the first; and weak stress on the others. See Test 29.

Schwa /ə/
Most very weak syllables contain **schwa**, which is the name of the shortest (and most common) spoken vowel found in English. The word 'economic' contains two written <o> vowels; but when written in phonemic script, /ˌekəˈnɒmik/, we see that the first very weak <o> is schwa, but <o> in the stressed syllable contains the longer sound found in 'top' and 'dog'. Schwa is also found in weak forms of most grammatical words such as 'to' and 'her'.

Pitch, tone groups and tonic syllables
Stressed syllables may change **pitch**. This means that the voice may move up or down. (Compare ↘'Yes' and ↗'Yes?') This change of pitch takes place on the most important syllable in a **tone group**, the **tonic syllable**. (See Test 22.) A sentence in terms of grammar/writing may consist of one or more tone groups. Compare 'the film was ↘**mar**vellous' (one tone group) with 'the ↘**film** | was ↘**mar**vellous' (two tone groups).

Intonation
Changes of pitch (see the above paragraph) are what make up the **intonation** of a language. In this book we concentrate on the two most important possible directions for the change of pitch: a **fall** (↘) or a **fall-rise** (↺).

Highlighting
We often use a **high fall** when a word is particularly important, especially when it is **highlighted**. Take the sequence 'I didn't want a black coffee; I ordered a ↘**WHITE** coffee.' The word *white* is highlighted because it contrasts with *black* and provides the most important new information. So the voice starts high on *white* and falls down to the bottom of the voice.

Symbols of the International Phonetic Alphabet

Vowels

short:

ɪ	bit, in
e	best, pen
æ	bad, cat
ʌ	cup, love
ɒ	dog, wash
ʊ	put, good
ə	potato, under
i	happy, lucky, stadium

long:

iː	sea, key
ɑː	car, start
ɔː	north, bought
uː	blue, new
ɜː	girl, fur

diphthongs:

eɪ	day, make
aɪ	try, night
ɔɪ	boy, noise
əʊ	no, low
aʊ	how, loud
ɪə	here, near
eə	there, wear
ʊə	cure, newer

Consonants

p	pen, top
b	back, job
t	time, bit
d	dog, bad
k	cat, pick
g	go, bag
f	find, off
v	view, save
θ	think, bath
ð	this, with
s	see, police
z	zero, please
ʃ	ship, station
ʒ	measure, television
h	head, whole
m	miss, climb
n	need, know
ŋ	sing, long
tʃ	check, pitch
dʒ	jam, age
l	like, feel
r	right, wrong
j	yes, year
w	wet, queen

1 Which sound? Names 1

Read the following sets of names and decide how you think they will be pronounced. Then listen to the recording and decide which order they appear in.

Example:
_2_ a) Jan Lipman _3_ b) Jane Lipman _1_ c) Jane Leapman
_4_ d) Jan Leapman

1 ____ a) Pete ____ b) Peter ____ c) Pet ____ d) Bet

2 ____ a) Mick Wilson ____ b) Mike Wilson ____ c) Mack Wilson
   ____ d) Mark Wilson

3 ____ a) Mary Pears ____ b) Marie Pierce ____ c) Mary Pierce
   ____ d) Marie Pears

4 ____ a) Lucille ____ b) Lucy ____ c) Lucia ____ d) Luke

5 ____ a) Peter Bales ____ b) Peter Vales ____ c) Pete Bales
   ____ d) Pete Vales

6 ____ a) Barbara Eaton ____ b) Barbara Heaton
   ____ c) Barbie Eaton ____ d) Barbie Heaton

7 ____ a) Joe Newman ____ b) Joan Newman ____ c) Jay Newman
   ____ d) Jane Newman

8 ____ a) Sir Ralph Grigson ____ b) Sir Alf Grigson
   ____ c) Sir Alf Gregson ____ d) Sir Ralph Gregson

9 ____ a) Bet ____ b) Beth ____ c) Betty ____ d) Bess

10 ____ a) Gert Fraser ____ b) Curt Frasier ____ c) Gert Frasier
   ____ d) Curt Fraser

11 ____ a) Rita Lennon ____ b) Lita Lemon ____ c) Lita Lennon
   ____ d) Rita Lenin

12 ____ a) Alec Shearer ____ b) Alex Shearer ____ c) Eric Shearer
   ____ d) Erica Shearer

13 ____ a) Carl Bley ____ b) Carla Bley ____ c) Carla Bligh
   ____ d) Carl Bligh

14 ____ a) Corin ____ b) Colin ____ c) Corinne ____ d) Karina

2 Which sound? Names 2

Listen to the recording and decide which names you hear.

Example: I've invited _____*Pete*_____ to join us.
    (a) Pete   b) Peter   c) Pet

1   *I've just been talking to _____*
    a) Jan Lipman b) Jane Lipman c) Jane Leapman d) Jan Leapman

2   *I've just got a letter from _____ .*
    a) Eryl   b) Meryl

3   *Can I speak to _____ , please.*
    a) Mick Wilson b) Mike Wilson c) Mack Wilson d) Mark Wilson

4   *I haven't seen _____ for ages.*
    a) Mary   b) Marie

5   *Could you give this to _____ , please?*
    a) Lucille   b) Lucy

6   *I think that's _____ over there.*
    a) Peter Bales   b) Peter Vales   c) Pete Bales   d) Pete Vales

7   *Have you ever met _____ ?*
    a) Barbara Eaton b) Barbara Heaton c) Barbie Eaton
    d) Barbie Heaton

8   *I've invited _____ as well.*
    a) Joe Newman   b) Joan Newman

9   *That's _____ , I think.*
    a) Sir Ralph   b) Sir Alf

10   *I think that's _____ over there.*
    a) Sue Weedon   b) Sue Eden

11   *Is _____ here today?*
    a) Gert   b) Curt

12   *I'm going with _____ to the cinema.*
    a) Alec   b) Alex

13   *Have you seen _____ recently?*
    a) Rita   b) Lita

14   *I hear that _____ has got a new job)*
    a) Bet   b) Beth   c) Betty   d) Bess

15   *Isn't that _____ over there?*
    a) Carl   b) Carla

3 Weak forms

Listen to the following sentences and fill each gap with one or more words. (Some verbs are in their abbreviated forms, e.g. *I've / he's / we'd*).

Example: __Would you__ like _____to_____ go ___to the___ canteen ____for a____ sandwich?

1 I'm going (a) _____ town (b) _____ half (c) _____ hour.

2 (a) _____ just got a present (b) _____ my father.

3 I think they (a) _____ gone (b) _____ library.

4 (a) _____ like (b) _____ glass (c) _____ two (d) _____ water.

5 They thanked me (a) _____ helping (b) _____ find the money.

6 (a) _____ know (b) _____ Mary is?

7 Last time I saw (a) _____ she (b) _____ on (c) _____ way (d) _____ town.

8 If (a) _____ been sensible (b) _____ listened (c) _____ my teacher.

9 Last night we went to a place (a) _____ lots of cafes.

Grammatical words, such as **prepositions** (e.g. *to*), **articles** (e.g. *the*), **pronouns** (e.g. *them*) and **modal** or **auxiliary verbs** (e.g. *have*), are usually found in very weak, short forms, often containing schwa (see page v). See Test 11 for strong forms.

4 How many sounds are the same?

Look at and listen to these pairs of words.

a) *Peter* and *pepper*. These start with the same consonant sound /p/, but the following vowel sound is different: /piːtə/ and /pepə/.

b) *Peter* and *pizza*. These start with the same three sounds: /piːtə/ and /piːtsə/.

Now read the following pairs of words. How many identical sounds do they start with? Listen to the recording to check how they are pronounced.

Examples:

Peter / pepper ___1___　　　　Peter / pizza ___3___

1	Kate / cake _____	9	Penny / pizza _____
2	Charles / chocolate _____	10	Margery / margarine _____
3	Oliver / olives _____	11	Barbara / bananas _____
4	Tom / tomatoes _____	12	Sam / salmon _____
5	Susan / sugar _____	13	Colin / cola _____
6	Salome / salami _____	14	Brenda / bread _____
7	Pat / pasta _____	15	Jim / gin _____
8	Patty / pastry _____	16	Raymond / radishes _____

5 Odd one out 1

A In each line, identify the word that has a different **first** consonant sound. Read them first, then listen to the recording to check.

Example: friend <u>priest</u> physical philosophy

1	kettle	car	circle	catch
2	these	thank	think	thread
3	when	which	whose	where
4	church	choir	cheap	chart
5	plenty	prince	piano	pneumatic
6	number	know	moon	gnaw

B In each line, identify the word that has a different **final** consonant sound. Then listen to the recording to check.

1	picked	rubbed	fact	bought
2	dragged	road	dropped	hide
3	cough	safe	roof	of
4	packs	ox	begs	pats
5	lump	chasm	limb	name
6	sock	music	arch	ache

6 Odd one out 2

A   Each line contains either verbs or adjectives ending in <-ed>, or verbs or nouns ending in <-s>. Decide which is the odd one out in terms of the way that the ending is pronounced. Then check your answer with the recording.

Example: seas   <u>picks</u>   pays   digs

1   picked   stopped   robbed   taped
2   wanted   shaped   estimated   congratulated
3   shops   digs   robs   codes
4   judges   horses   names   wishes
5   trapped   faked   hoped   faded
6   wicked   picked   tricked   licked

B   In each line, identify the word that has a different vowel sound.

1   sun   son   done   on
2   make   leak   break   steak
3   cap   packed   patted   waste
4   grave   have   save   cape
5   fool   wood   look   put
6   queue   tool   group   loud
7   give   strive   five   hive
8   cute   must   muse   news

7 Odd one out 3

A   How many syllables?
One word in each set has a different number of syllables from the others. Decide which it is, then check with the recording.

Example: lengths   if   <u>table</u>   on

1	destiny	chocolate	computer	afterwards
2	stopped	smashed	wanted	tried
3	Leicester	Lester	Stratford	Manchester
4	altogether	avocado	banana	Argentina
5	rhythm	chasm	through	thorough

B   What stress pattern?
One word in each set has a different stress pattern from the others. Which is it? Check with the recording.

Example: picture □o   nature □o   capture □o   <u>mature</u> o□

1	politics	dynamic	musician	historic
2	create	supply	prostate	dictate
3	teacher	refer	eager	offer
4	edit	debit	submit	credit
5	Angela	Theresa	spaghetti	banana

The pronunciation of proper names – especially place names – has changed over the years. In many names the final syllable has become very weak, often containing the schwa vowel (see page v) – for example, Oxford, Nottingham, Leicester, Stratford.

8 Short or long vowels?

Read the following names and decide, from their spelling, if the vowel is **short** or **long**. (If there is more than one vowel, focus on the vowel receiving most stress.) If you are not sure, check the recording.

Example: Mick = short   Susan = long

Mick	Susan	Dean	Sammy	Cathy
Martha	Jane	Luke	Tammy	Rose
Bert	Muriel	Patty	Pete	Ross
Ted	David	Becky	Bud	Simon
Beth	Mike	Mary	Tom	Jean
Timmy	Joan	Bonnie	Sheila	Bill

Short vowel sound	Long vowel sound

The vowel sound is generally **short** if the (written) vowel is followed by
a) a single consonant: *Bud, Tom, Ted,* or
b) two consonants: *Sammy, Beth, Ross*
The vowel sound is generally **long** if the (written) vowel is followed by
a) the letter <r>: *Martha, Bert,* or
b) a single consonant followed by a vowel: *Muriel, Pete, David, Simon,* or
c) if the vowel sound is represented by two written vowels: *Dean, Sheila*

9 Word stress 1

Read the following two-syllable words and decide if the stress is on the first or last syllable. Then listen to the recording to see if you are right.

Example: table ☐ o elect o ☐ cancel ☐ o

repeat	edit	teacher	surprise
manage	bottle	listen	below
above	under	royal	postpone
allow	collect	limit	vanish
picture	forgive	funny	believe
village	sweeten	prefer	cover
after	lucky	former	local

Most two-syllable **nouns** have front stress (= stress on the first syllable, ☐ o). Most two-syllable **verbs**, by contrast, have end stress (= stress on the last syllable, o ☐) except if the second syllable **must** be weak. (See the Answers for exceptions.)

10 Word stress 2

Test 9 showed that most two-syllable nouns have front stress, and most two-syllable verbs have end stress. Some words, with identical spelling, have **front** stress if used as a **noun**, and **end** stress if used as a **verb**. Listen to these two examples.

The group has just reCORded a new REcord. (record)

IMports have gone up recently. In fact we are imPORting twice as much as last year. (import)

Now place the following words (which can be either noun or verb) in the box below.

repeat	subject	varnish	contrast	rebel	rewrite
damage	escape	answer	increase	present	credit
debate	object	export	regret	suspect	fiddle
treasure	reply	replay	produce	account	pervert

Always ☐○	**Always** ○☐	☐○ **when it is a noun** ○☐ **when it is a verb**
varnish	*repeat*	*subject*

11 Weak or strong?

Decide if the underlined words are likely to be in their weak form or their strong form.

	weak	strong
Example:		
Who did you give the money <u>to</u>?		✓
<u>To</u> my sister.	✓	

		weak	strong
1	I'd like a cup <u>of</u> coffee.	_____	_____
2	– My sister used to go out with Elvis.		
	– Not <u>the</u> Elvis!	_____	_____
3	What's your dress made <u>of</u>?	_____	_____
4	That's <u>her</u>! Over there!	_____	_____
5	– <u>Do</u> you like jazz?	_____	_____
	– Yes, I <u>do</u>.	_____	_____
6	I'm going to study maths <u>and</u> physics,	_____	_____
	but I'm not sure <u>where</u>.	_____	_____
7	– Who's that letter <u>from</u>?	_____	_____
	– <u>From</u> my parents.	_____	_____
8	I really like rock <u>and</u> roll.	_____	_____
9	– Which did you order? Fish or meat?		
	– I ordered fish <u>and</u> meat. I'm feeling hungry.	_____	_____

The strong form of pronunciation of a word is usually found:
a) When it ends a sequence. *What is it made <u>of</u>?*
b) When it gives new information or stands alone. *Who did you give it to?
Her!*
c) When it contrasts with another word. *I gave it to <u>her</u>, not <u>him</u>.*

12 Contrastive stress 1

When we stress a word very strongly (especially when we correct someone) there is usually a very high fall on the most important syllable. Listen to the following:

    A. So you were born in the South of ⇘**Eng**land.

    B. No, I was born in the ⇘**NORTH** of England.

Did you hear how in A the voice fell gently on the first syllable of *England*? In B, by contrast, the main stress shifted to *North*, the word which provided new information, and the fall came from much higher.

Now listen to A, below. Then read the prompts for B, and work out B's response. Say your response aloud, then listen to the recording to check.

Example:

    A. Here's the cheese ⇘sandwich you wanted.

    B. / that's wrong / ordered / meat sandwich /

    → That's ⇘**wrong**. I ordered a ⇘**MEAT** sandwich.

1   A. OK, that's two white ⇘coffees.

       B. / No / always drink / black coffee /

2   A. So, your daughter sells ⇘clothes.

       B. / No / daughter / makes clothes /

3   A. I used to live in the South of ⇘France, like ⇘you.

       B. / No / used to live / South / Italy /

4   A. Would you like some potato ⇗soup for lunch later on?

       B. / prefer / fish soup / if that's OK /

5   A. You're a com⇘puter operator, I understand.

       B. / No / computer programmer /

6   A. Did you buy that cotton ⬀shirt you were looking at?

      B. / No / silk shirt / instead

7   A. Would you like to sit out⬎side?

      B. / prefer / sit / inside / if possible.

8   A. Do you fancy fish and ⬎chips?

      B. / rather have / chicken and chips /

9   A. So your mother's ⬎Welsh.

      B. / No / father / Welsh /

10 A. Let's meet at half past ⬎ten.

      B. / rather meet / quarter / ten /

11 A. So your partner is John ⬎Smith.

      B. / No / partner / Jane Smith /

12 A. So your son's going to play for Manchester ⬎City.

      B. / No, he's / play for / Manchester United /

13 A. So your son's going to play for Leeds U⬎nited.

      B. / No, he's / play for / Manchester United /

14 A. Let's meet at quarter past ⬎nine.

      B. / think / better meet / quarter to /

 In a high contrastive **fall**, the voice starts high and goes smoothly down, to the bottom of the voice.

13 Contrastive stress 2

Listen to the following sentence beginnings and underline a, b, c or d to show how you think each sentence will continue. Then check with the recording.

1 **Example:**

I didn't paint the house YESterday ...

a) ... I **CLEANED** it.

b) ... **LIN**da did.

c) <u>... I did it on SATurday.</u>

d) ... I painted the GArage.

---

2 Joe didn't buy the house in nineteen ninety-six ...

a) ... that's when he **SOLD** it.

b) ... it was nineteen **EIGH**ty-six.

c) ... it was his **BRO**ther.

d) ... it was nineteen ninety-**FIVE**.

---

3 I didn't paint the house yesterday ...

a) ... I **CLEANED** it.

b) ... **LIN**da did.

c) ... I did it on SAturday.

d) ... I painted the GArage.

---

4 Joe didn't buy the house in nineteen ninety-six ...

a) ... that's when he **SOLD** it.

b) ... it was nineteen **EIGH**ty-six.

c) ... it was his **BRO**ther.

d) ... it was nineteen ninety-**FIVE**.

5 I didn't paint the house yesterday ...

    a) ... I **CLEANED** it.

    b) ... **LIN**da did.

    c) ... I did it on **SA**turday.

    d) ... I painted the **GA**rage.

---

6 Joe didn't buy the house in nineteen ninety-six ...

    a) ... that's when he **SOLD** it.

    b) ... it was nineteen **EIGH**ty-six.

    c) ... it was his **BRO**ther.

    d) ... it was nineteen ninety-**FIVE**.

---

7 I didn't paint the house yesterday ...

    a) ... I **CLEANED** it.

    b) ... **LIN**da did.

    c) ... I did it on **SA**turday.

    d) ... I painted the **GA**rage.

---

8 Joe didn't buy the house in nineteen ninety-six ...

    a) ... that's when he **SOLD** it.

    b) ... it was nineteen **EIGH**ty-six.

    c) ... it was his **BRO**ther

    d) ... it was nineteen ninety-**FIVE**.

We normally contrast words of the same grammatical type. So, in the first example, the time adverb *yesterday* contrasts with *Saturday*.

14 Predicting contrastive stress

In each of these sentences some words are contrasted and will be heavily stressed. Read the sentences and underline the syllables that you predict will be heavily stressed. Then listen to the recording to see if you are right.

Example: I don't know ↘JANE↗ Smith, but I ↘do know her ↘hus↗band ↘JOHN Smith.

1 I've got one sister, and my wife has two sisters.

2 I didn't say we'd meet at quarter to six; I said quarter past six!

3 My sister was born in 1959, and my wife in 1969.

4 Joe lives in North America, and Pablo in South America.

5 Diesel engines cause more pollution than petrol engines.

6 I've never been to South America, but I have been to South Africa.

7 My grandfather was born in 1904; and my grandmother was born in 1905.

8 He served not only in the First World War, but also in the Second World War.

9 Don't let's go on the 21st; let's make it the 28th.

10 I don't live in the outskirts of London; I live right in the centre of London.

It is important not just to know which syllables are to be **stressed**; you should also try to imitate the **intonation**. So note where there is a **fall-rise** (↻) and where there is a straight **fall** (↘) .

15 Changing sounds 1 Elision

In normal, fast spoken English, certain sounds may disappear. Listen to the following sentences and spot the times when the sounds /t/ or /d/ may disappear.

Example: Let's face the fac~~t~~s. This company is going bus~~y~~ quickly.

1. My landlady bought a new handbag the other day.

2. The first girl earned twenty pounds.

3. The second boy waited for half an hour.

4. I don't know when they finished work yesterday.

5. I don't like fast food as a rule.

6. It was a perfect afternoon, perfectly marvellous.

7. Raise both your hands slowly into the air.

8. I watch TV most evenings; in fact I watched for five hours last night.

This disappearance of sounds is known as elision; the sounds are elided. The two sounds /t/ and /d/ are frequently elided, especially when they are found between two other consonants. So:
- we will hear the /t/ in *fact*, but not in *facts*, and
- we will hear the /d/ in *land*, but not in *landlady*.

This means even negative /t/, and the final /d/ or /t/ in past tenses and passives, may disappear:
- *I don'(t) know.*
- *I watch(ed) TV las(t) night.*

16 Changing sounds 2 Assimilation

In normal, fast speech some consonant sounds may change so that we can pass easily from one word to another.

Example: /n/   *ten boys*   sounds like   *tem boys*
              ten girls   sounds like   *teng girls*

Read the following sentences and try to spot the consonants which are likely to change when spoken fast. Then check with the recording.

1   Make sure everything's in place, in case they arrive early.

2   Instead of taking the bus, let's walk through Green Park and Hyde Park.

3   That's the third person I've seen wearing a red coat this morning.

4   Would you prefer eggs and bacon or sausages and mashed potatoes?

5   I spend half the year in Paris and the rest in Berlin.

6   The only thing I keep in my handbag is a purse and a handkerchief.

I spend half the year in Paris and the rest in Berlin.

 This type of change of sound is known as **assimilation**. In the examples we see how /n/ may change to /m/ (in front of /m/, /p/, /b/ and /w/) or to /ŋ/ (in front of /k/ and /g/). But other consonants may also change. In the test you will hear that /d/ becomes /b/ or /g/ depending on the following sound.

17 Changing sounds 3
Elision and assimilation

In the following sentences, the words in **bold** show how certain words or phrases sound in ordinary, fast speech. Work out how they should really be written.

Example: A Hollywood studio wants to film my **scream-play**!
= *screenplay*

1   Tonight there are likely to be some **miss patches** in the North.

2   The **pry minister** is due to visit Russia within the next few weeks.

3   Careful on that street. There's a lot of **bag guys** there.

4   The **neck strain** will be arriving at platform 2 in five minutes.

5   I **wooden chews** that one if I were you.

6   I'm not hungry. I'll just have a **letter salad**, I think.

7   I really ought to buy some new **close**.

8   He was blown up by a **lamb-mine**.

9   There were **sick students** waiting for the teacher.

10   You shouldn't stay under a **sum-bed** too long or you'll burn.

11   The prisoner was taken away wearing **hang-cuffs**.

12   Their goods were kept in **coal storage** for months.

13   No, I don't want a burger. I don't like **farce food**.

14   I'm not really a **cap person**. I much prefer dogs.

15   I think England last won the **Whirl Cup** over 30 years ago.

16   We'd better **face the fax**. They're not going to accept our offer.

17   We've got to go ahead. Now's not the time to get **coal feet**.

18   Hey, **mine the gap**! It's really wide on this platform.

19   Sorry, this is a private party. If you're not on the **guess list** you can't get in.

20   The defendant pleaded **knock guilty**.

21   Can you lend me **sick squid** till Friday?

22   There were **ache girls** and **ape boys** at the party.

23   (Of course, these things only happen in **farce peach**.)

18 Pausing, stress and intonation

What are these people saying? Listen to the recording, and decide which sequence comes first.

Example: a) I'm going to.   (2)
              b) I'm going, too. (1)

1   a) I'm afraid they can't.
    b) I'm afraid. They can't.

2   a) I don't. No.
    b) I don't know.

3   a) I don't know, John.
    b) I don't know John.

4   a) My aunt who lives in Leeds is coming for Christmas.
    b) My aunt, who lives in Leeds, is coming for Christmas.

5   a) I met the chief Executive (Mary Smith) and the Company
       Secretary. (= 2 people)
    b) I met the Chief Executive, Mary Smith, and the Company
       Secretary. (= 3 people)

6   a) I bought them for dogs.
    b) I bought them four dogs.

7   a) – What should I do? – Obey Angela.
    b) – What should I do? – Obey, Angela.

8   a) 'Joe', said the boss, 'is stupid.'
    b) Joe said the boss is stupid.

9   a) I'm going to see Uncle Ken.
    b) I'm going to sea, Uncle Ken.

19 Identifying vowel sounds

Place the following words in the grids according to their vowel sound.

rich/ curl / death / month / shone / lawn / cart / suit / breathe / flashed /
loom / herd / still / earn / hemmed / poured / torn / scene / cruise /
floor / dock / just / would / don / sword / hoop / banned / rang / bin /
love / hat / bird / stabbed / hood / farm / ought / ridge / ton / cloth /
chalk / hoot / son / link / next / calm / germ / hymn / cab / wood /
breath / creep / itch / blood / cough / should / could / black / said /
foot / monk / dog / stood / piece / arch / move / purr / feast / palm /
pearl / edge / shopped / eve / barred / soup / leaf / bard / begged

Short vowel sounds

pit pɪt	pat pæt	pet pet	putt pʌt	pot pɒt	put pʊt

Long vowel sounds

peat piːt	pert pɜːt	part pɑːt	port pɔːt	boot buːt

20 Predicting highlighting shift in dialogue 1

In conversation, the emphasis shifts as new, important words come in. The new words are highlighted. Listen to these examples, and compare them.

1) A. Where did you go in the summer? B. The South of ↘FRANCE.
2) A. Which part of France do you prefer? B. The ↘SOUTH of France.

Now read the following conversations aloud. Predict which is the most important syllable of the most important word in each sentence. Underline that syllable. Then listen to the recording.

Example: – I fancy seeing a **film**.

– What **kind** of film?

– Oh, **any** kind of film.

– How about a **comedy**?

– I can't **stand** comedies. I'd rather see an **action** movie.

1 – Where did you put the potatoes?

– Where do you think I put the potatoes? There's only one place to put them!

– Well, I can't find them!

– They're in the cupboard.

– But I've looked in the cupboard.

– You can't have looked in the cupboard.

– Well, I have.

– Sorry … they're still in the shopping bag.

2 – Where are you spending your holidays?

– In France.

– Where in France?

– The south.

– I've never been to the south of France. But I've lived in the south of Spain.

– Where exactly in the south?

– In Seville.

– That's a coincidence. My daughter lives in Seville!

– Which of your daughters?

– Susan, my eldest daughter.

– What's she doing there?

– Working as a teacher. An English teacher.

 In the first examples, in 1B *France* is the most important word, so it is highlighted. In 2B (where the wording is identical), *South* has become the most important word because it gives new information, *France* having been mentioned already in 2A.

21 Stress in phrases and compound nouns

Listen to the following two sentences:

a) *I was born in that green ↘HOUSE.* (phrase)
b) *We grow our tomatoes in that ↘GREENhouse.* (compound noun)

In (a), the words *green* and *house* form a phrase, and mean something different from the compound noun *greenhouse* in (b).

Now read the following sentences and decide if the words underlined are **phrases** or **compound nouns**. Then check by listening to the recording.

1   I went to the <u>shopping centre</u> to buy myself a couple of <u>cotton shirts</u>.

2   I think I've left my <u>car keys</u> in my <u>handbag</u>.

3   Would you prefer to visit the <u>White House</u> or <u>Buckingham Palace</u>?

4   We live in <u>Cambridge Avenue</u>, which is just off the <u>High Street</u>.

5   They own a <u>cotton factory</u> and several <u>steel mills</u> in <u>South America</u>.

6   Did you order a <u>cheese sandwich</u> and some <u>orange juice</u>?

a) *green ↘HOUSE*
- means 'a house which is green'
- is a **phrase**
- main stress on last element
- the last element may be tonic (= the main syllable may change pitch)

b) *↘GREENhouse*
- means 'a place for growing plants'
- is a **compound noun**
- main stress on first element
- the first element may be tonic

Place names, such as *Oxford Circus, Waterloo Bridge, Paddington Station, Lexington Avenue, New York, Piccadilly Circus,* etc., are usually **phrases**. The one exception is when the last element is *Street* (*Oxford Street,* for example), in which case they are **compounds**.

22 Sentence stress and tonic syllables

Listen to the recording of the following sentences, then show

a) the stressed syllables, by underlining;
b) the tonic syllables, by double underlining.

Example: I'm <u>go</u>ing to <u><u>town</u></u> to <u><u>buy</u></u> some <u><u>fruit</u></u> and <u><u>veg</u></u>etables.

1   I always visit my parents in the summer.

2   Do you fancy a cup of coffee?

3   My aunt and uncle live in the North of England.

4   Remind me to pick the children up from school at four o'clock.

5   I don't know John Smith, but I know his sister Jane Smith.

6   I think we'll eat in the dining-room, for a change.

7   I'd like to speak to Thomas, if he's in.

8   Susie suggested we meet at the station.

9   Conrad composed a concerto for trumpet.

10   What's that shirt made of?

A tonic syllable is not just stressed. It also involves a change of **pitch**. If no stressed syllable in a tone group is more important than any other, then the tonic syllable is found in the last stressed word (*vegetables*, in the example).

23 Grouping rhyming words 1

Place these words in the grids according to how they rhyme.

alert / bean / between / canned / complain / convene / core / cork / curt / delight / design / earl / four / furl / gate / hand / hawk / height / hurl / hurt / incite / insane / kite / land / mean / pane / pearl / pert / pine / polite / raw / refine / refrain / reign / relate / resign / roar / scene / shirt / shore / sign / spanned / stalk / state / stork / tanned / wait / walk / weight / whirl

/iːn/	/eɪn/	/eɪt/	/ɔː/	/aɪn/
seen	main	hate	law	wine

/ænd/	/ɜːt/	/ɜːl/	/ɔːk/	/aɪt/
band	dirt	girl	fork	white

Words which **rhyme** always have the same vowel sound in the main stressed syllable, e.g. *show* and *go*; *sea* and *tree* – here the words end with the vowel sound. Words also rhyme if the rhyming vowel sound is followed by the same consonant sound, e.g. *long* and *wrong*; *rose* and *suppose* – or by a number of sounds: *fact* and *packed*; *ending* and *bending*.

Some difficult words? – read the tip for Test 24.

24 Grouping rhyming words 2

Place these words in the grids according to how they rhyme.

act / aloft / atone / beast / break / caught / ceased / chew / confer /
coughed / demur / doffed / fir / flu / fort / fought / fur / gist / hissed /
insist / jerk / kissed / least / list / loan / loft / lone / mown / opaque /
perk / pieced / purr / quake / retract / sacked / sewn / shirk / smirk /
shake / snort / steak / taught / threw / through / too / tracked / Turk /
waft / whacked / yeast

/əʊn/	/uː/	/ɜː/	/ɔːt/	/iːst/
phone	who	sir	court	east

/ɜːk/	/eɪk/	/ɪst/	/ækt/	/ɒft/
work	make	mist	pact	soft

Tests 23 to 25 contain words that you may not know – but you don't need
to know the meanings, and you can look them up in a dictionary afterwards
if you want to. The aim of these tests is to help you predict the
pronunciation of words you don't know, by looking at their spelling.

25 Grouping rhyming words 3

Place these words in the grids according to how they rhyme.

alarm / backs / balm / bird / boom / calm / charm / charred /
conveyed / course / curd / displayed / fax / firm / flawed / force /
gloom / gorse / groom / hard / heard / herd / hoarse / horde / lard /
loon / maid / noon / parade / pawed / perm / poured / prune / psalm /
relax / sacks / sauce / shacks / snored / sparred /spurred / squirm /
starred / strewn / term / tomb / tune / weighed / womb / worm

/ɜːd/	/ɔːd/	/ɑːm/	/ɑːd/	/eɪd/
word	board	farm	card	shade

/æks/	/ɜːm/	/uːn/	/uːm/	/ɔːs/
axe	germ	June	loom	Morse

26 Predicting pronunciation and spelling 1

A Here are twelve pairs of rhyming words. In each case, one has an expected spelling for the particular sound and one has not. Choose which is the more predictable spelling.

Example: cheque <u>neck</u>
(compare *neck* with *peck, deck, wreck, speck* and so on)

1	droop soup	5	rich stitch	9	file style
2	mash cache	6	chest breast	10	taste waist
3	steak make	7	wand bond	11	worm squirm
4	moon prune	8	blood mud	12	tomb loom

B And here are some pairs of words which look as though they should rhyme, but don't. Choose the one which has the more predictable relationship between pronunciation and spelling.

1	cut put	5	bear fear	9	call shall
2	warm charm	6	cork work	10	word lord
3	worm storm	7	wart dart	11	dome some
4	boot foot	8	said maid	12	want pant

 Many people think that English spelling is completely illogical. And yet the pronunciation of about 95% of all words is predictable from the spelling.

27 Predicting pronunciation and spelling 2

A In this section the spelling is **100% predictable** from the pronunciation. Listen to the recording and write these individual words down.

1	_____	5	_____	9	_____	13	_____
2	_____	6	_____	10	_____	14	_____
3	_____	7	_____	11	_____	15	_____
4	_____	8	_____	12	_____	16	_____

B Now see if you can read the following words aloud before you listen to them on the recording. Remember that the pronunciation is still predictable from the spelling.

1	scoop	5	patched	9	puddle	13	shun
2	muted	6	rotter	10	stutter	14	candle
3	glitch	7	hugged	11	handy	15	rumbled
4	spine	8	treck	12	budge	16	trash

C Now do the same with the following nonsense words.

1	flape	5	snork	9	frake	13	spump
2	spline	6	preck	10	drumble	14	flinge
3	smotted	7	glumpy	11	duddle	15	chinker
4	gatter	8	chandy	12	shunker	16	strended

It doesn't matter if you don't know what the words in A and B mean; you can always check them in a dictionary afterwards. Don't look in a dictionary for the nonsense words in C!

28 Find the rhymes 1

Here are some very short, two-line poems, but the rhyming words are missing. Try to guess the missing words which complete each poem. If you can't think of any, choose them from the list. (The list contains some words which rhyme, but which do not make sense in the poems.)

1

'It's always _____

Down on the _____'

2

'I think you _____

To leave the _____'

3

'I like a _____

Last thing at _____'

4

'You haven't _____

A single _____'

5

Yes, mum

'She's learned to _____

In just a _____'

bike / bird / bite / bought / byte / calm / caught / charm / court / farm / feel / fight / harm / heard / herd / leak / leek / light / like / listened / meal / might / night / ought / right / should / sight / speak / spoken / talk / taught / token / walk / weak / week / wood / word / work

Word stress 3 Primary and secondary stress

A Look at the grid below while you listen to the words on the recording. Then listen again and say the words at the same time as you hear them, giving special emphasis to the stressed syllables.

weak stress ○	SECONDARY STRESS □	weak stress ○	PRIMARY STRESS □	weak stress ○	weak stress ○
		de	**CI**	sion	
			MU	sic	al
	UN	der	**STAND**		
	CON	dem	**NA**	tion	
		com	**MU**	ni	cate
	CRE	di	**BI**	li	ty
pro	NUN	ci	**A**	tion	

Numbers alongside rows: 1, 2, 3, 4, 5, 6, 7

B Now look at the words below and see if you can place each word in the grid opposite, according to its stress pattern. Use the recording to check.

editor / refugee / hallucination / ultimatum / departure / journalistic / interfere / afterwards / survivable / determination / oceanographer / mistranslate / musician / overpaid / conductivity / investigation / existential / seasickness / banana / congratulations / potato / customer / commemorate / inexcusable / computer / productivity / luckily / California / indecision / exhibitionist / expandable / survival / productive / chemistry / activate / avocado / executive

1	○ □ ○	decision
2	□ ○ ○	musical *editor*
3	□ ○ □	understand
4	□ ○ □ ○	condemnation
5	○ □ ○ ○	communicate
6	□ ○ □ ○ ○	credibility
7	○ □ ○ □ ○	pronunciation

In two-syllable words, a syllable is either strong or weak (see Tests 9 and 10). But in some three-syllable words, and in most words of four syllables or more, there are two stressed syllables: one carries **primary** (or **main**) stress, the other **secondary** stress.

30 Find the rhymes 2

Here are some very short, two-line poems, but the rhyming words are missing.
Try to guess the missing words which complete each poem. If you can't think
of any, choose them from the list. (The list contains some words which rhyme,
but which do not make sense in the poems.)

1

'This shirt you _____

Is rather _____'

4

'It's not too _____

To lose some _____'

2

'I think I'll _____

A pound of _____'

5

'I wish the _____

Would make less _____'

3

'He learned to _____

In just one _____'

bought / boys / buy / by / caught / day / height / kids / late / light /
mate / meat / meet / night / noise / play / poem / read / reed / right /
shake / short / soon / sound / steak / take / toys / wait / weigh /
weight / write

31 Spot the homophones 1

Homophones are words (or combinations of words) which sound the same, but are spelled differently and have different meanings: e.g. *meet* and *meat*, *seen* and *scene*. Find the pairs of homophones hidden in the list below.

side / balls / bear / bowled / cue / ducked / fort /

work / grate / hair / hare / bales / week / dally /

bald / hold / fought / weekly / stoke / walk /

missed / air / pure / packed / pear / pore / where /

pour / duct / bore / seam / quiet / sought / please /

shake / wade / sheikh / pleas / weakly / bold / past /

sighed / piece / mist / wear / seem / sight / slay /

wake / win / steak / stalk / stroke / stork / daily /

stake / weak / bare / holed / wine / pact / bawls /

passed / wane / queue / great / heir / pair / whine /

grant / sleigh / same / weighed / site / peace

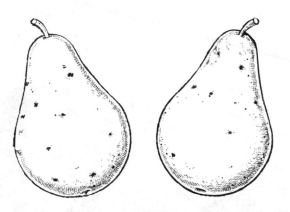

A pair of pears

 Some of these words do not form pairs of homophones.

32 Spot the homophones 2

This is like Test 31, but with two differences.

a) There are some examples of **one** word sounding like a **combination** of words (e.g. *heed* and *he'd*), and

b) sometimes **three** words (or combinations of words) sound exactly the same, e.g. *I'll*, *isle* and *aisle*.

isle / bard / beer / bored / caught / night /
pale /cawed / chord / sly / died / dyer / cored /
dough / flawed / toed / pear / meal / floored /
teas / knew / heard / soar / heal / lacks / lax /
male / steer / we'll / maize / might / slay /
dead / stair / mite / breaks / knight / towed /
dire / knit / weight / herd / seam / aisle / he'll /
nit / tees / new / pail / bier / board / barred /
pare / doe / pair / rain / court / bared / dyed /
heel / reign / saw / mail / sore / I'll / seem /
maze / sleigh / stare / tease / toad / wait / wheel

 Some of these words do not form pairs of homophones.

33 Spot the homophones 3

In the following conversation a large number of words have been replaced by homophones. Spot where they have been used and decide how the words should be written.

– Lousy whether we've been having recently. (= Lousy **weather**...)

– We haven't been having much son, that's for shore. I got court in the reign this mourning and got wet threw.

– Me two. And how about that cold missed first thing? I went out bear-headed to get sum fire-would and haven't bean warm since. And my hands got quite saw as well. Really roar, they feel.

– I no watcher mean. I always get aches and panes in the winter. Anyway, weir off to get some son necks tweak. Weave booked a few daze in Singerpoor.

– Yes, I herd you had. Lucky yew! Still, I shouldn't mown. We flue to Florida last cheer, witch was really nice, and it's only fore weeks till we visit my sun and daughter-in-lore in Roam. Haven't scene them for rages. We only maid the booking yesterday, threw the internet. Mary's already pact; she can't weight.

– Well, tell her she won't knead her fir coat any weigh.

– Rite. Oh Kay. Aisle sea you later.

– Buy. See ewe a round.

 Some of the homophones show that this is fast, informal speech.

34 Spoonerisms

A Spoonerism is one sort of mistake in pronunciation, where the consonant sounds at the start of two words (or a group of words) are swapped.

Examples: You have **t**asted a whole **w**orm. (= You have **w**asted a whole **t**erm.)

a **bl**ushing **cr**ow (= a **cr**ushing **bl**ow)

The following text is full of Spoonerisms (shown in **bold**). See if you can work out how the words should be written.

Sunday morning …

We live in an old **bread rick** house in Sussex. The **heather's** been really **what** the last month or so. In fact we've never known such **hummer seat**. Most mornings there's a **might list** at first, but that clears away quickly, leaving a fine **dunny say**. But some mornings have started with a **fence dog**.

Anyway, when I **mow cup** this **warning** I was expecting another lovely **dot hummer say**. But when I looked outside I saw that it was **roaring** with **pain**, and it felt so cold that I decided to **fight a liar**. Then I spent a happy twenty minutes in the bath **beading a rook**. My **life win** prefers to **shake a tower**, but I always like to **toke** in a hot **sub**.

After breakfast I **chord** myself a final **pup** of coffee, then settled back to **mead** yesterday's **rail**, which I'd been too busy to deal with. There was a **stole hack** of **monk jail**, as usual, but I was pleased to **pet** a **ghost-card** from my **dumb** and **mad**, who were spending a few **rays** in **Dome**.

It was **rhyme** to get **teddy** for church, so I put on my best **toot** and **sigh** with black **Susan shocks** while Lyn decided to wear the **silly** pink **fruit** she'd bought at the Harrods' sale.

Unfortunately, when I tried to **cart** the **star** I found that I had a **bat flattery**. Luckily, my next **poor** neighbour **Denny** helped me out, and we were soon on the road.

Remember that Spoonerisms affect **sounds**.

Spoonerisms are named after the Reverend William Spooner (1844–1930), a Cambridge academic who often used to make this kind of mistake. The first example at the top of the page is something he once said.

35 Using phonemic script 1

Write, in normal script, the names of these cities. (See page vi.)

'lʌndən _London_	beɪ'(d)ʒɪŋ	'pærɪs
rəʊm	'təʊkɪəʊ	'mæntʃəstə
'liːmə	hel'sɪŋki	ˌnjuː 'jɔːk
'kɑːdɪf	bɜː'lɪn	bel'greɪd
mə'drɪd	'braɪt(ə)n	'wɔːsɔː
'wɒʃɪŋtən	bɑːθ	ˌlɒs 'ændʒəliːz
'kiːtəʊ	səʊl	'venɪs

The small vertical line (') in a phonetic transcription shows the main stressed syllable within the word. The mark always appears *before* the stressed syllable, as in:

   'lʌndən   mə'drɪd   'kiːtəʊ   bɜː'lɪn

The small vertical line at the bottom of the line (ˌ) shows a secondary stress, as in:

   ˌnjuː 'jɔːk   ˌlɒs 'ændʒəliːz

See Test 29 for main (primary) stress and secondary stress.

36 Using phonemic script 2

Here are some names of cities and countries. Write them all in phonemic script, using the symbols from Test 35.

Prague

praːg

Lisbon

_____

Dublin

_____

Brussels

_____

Hungary

_____

Moscow

_____

Hamburg

_____

Geneva

_____

Japan

_____

Brazil

_____

Thailand

_____

Germany

_____

Wales

_____

England

_____

Scotland

_____

Bangkok

_____

Italy

_____

Korea

_____

China

_____

Manila

_____

Amsterdam

_____

Jakarta

_____

Greece

_____

Turkey

_____

 Some of the names have alternative pronunciations:

1) The weak syllable of *Thailand* and *Korea* can have either schwa or another sound.

2) Schwa itself may disappear. In *Brighton* and *Italy*, this is because final /n/ and /l/ may be 'syllabic consonants', with no vowel needed. In the case of *Hungary* the /g/ and /r/ need no vowel between, which means it can sound like *hungry*, especially when we speak fast.

3) In the case of *Amsterdam* there is an optional /p/ sound, as well as two possible stress patterns.

37 Correcting mistakes 1

You will hear several sentences describing each picture. But each sentence contains a mistake which you have to correct. Use the form of **contrastive stress** shown in Tests 12 to 14. The start of each correction is given.

Picture 1

a) No, there's a
   CAT on the table.

b) No, it's ...

c) No, it's ...

d) No, it's ...

Picture 2

a) No, she's ...

b) No, he's ...

c) No, she's ...

d) No, he ...

Picture 3

a) No, she's ...

b) No, he's ...

c) No, she's ...

d) No, he's ...

Picture 4

a) No, there are ...

b) No, it's ...

c) No, they're ...

d) No, she's ...

38 Correcting mistakes 2
Two-part correction

Look at the example below, then listen to the recording to see why we call this a 'two-part' correction.

Text   The Globe Theatre is on the South Bank of the river Thames.

Recording   The Globe Theatre is on the North Bank of the river Thames.

Correction Not the ⬊NORTH ⬈Bank; the ⬊SOUTH Bank.

Now read this tourist information about London. Then listen to the recording, where each statement has a mistake in it. Say your correction aloud after each statement, and listen to the correction on the recording.

The two most important parts of London, the West End and the City, are on the North Bank of the river Thames. The City, originally founded by the Romans, is the financial centre, where you will find most banks, insurance firms and trading companies. Until the 1950s, the tallest building in the City was Saint Paul's Cathedral, rebuilt after the Great Fire of 1666. But now the City is full of much taller buildings, often the headquarters of financial institutions.

The West End is full of shops, theatres, cinemas and restaurants. Most department stores are found in Oxford Street, while the largest toy shop in Britain, Hamleys, is in Regent Street, just south of Oxford Circus. Westminster is famous for the Houses of Parliament and Westminster Abbey, where the kings and queens of England are crowned. And the West End is where you will find several great museums and galleries, including the British Museum and the National Gallery.

More and more tourists are beginning to visit the South Bank, especially the cultural centre near Waterloo Bridge: this includes the National Theatre, with its three stages; the National Film Theatre; and three concert halls, the largest of which is the Royal Festival Hall. If you walk farther east along the riverside you will come to Tate Modern (the modern art building opposite Saint Paul's, converted from a power station) and the Globe Theatre, a reconstruction of the theatre where many of Shakespeare's plays were originally performed in the early seventeenth century.

There is a **fall-rise** in the first part of the correction – where we are **referring** to what has been said. There is a **fall** in the second part – where we are giving the new, correct information.

39 Odd one out 4

Each line contains three words that rhyme and one word that doesn't. Choose the odd one out.

Example: steel   peal   <u>stale</u>   peel

1	Bert	Curt	shirt	Bart
2	coot	loot	soot	shoot
3	relate	fete	weight	height
4	spook	took	look	rook
5	food	mood	brewed	good
6	sewed	glued	chewed	nude
7	jerk	clerk	work	shirk
8	pact	backed	baked	fact
9	scene	sign	mean	convene
10	laze	phase	days	size
11	peak	steak	leak	cheek
12	soot	cut	put	foot
13	height	tight	weight	might
14	stalk	work	fork	cork
15	quite	night	lied	light
16	clear	bear	hare	fair
17	barred	bared	hard	yard
18	duke	spook	look	Luke
19	taught	court	snort	coughed
20	prised	missed	fist	kissed

40 Word stress 4
Words and phrases

A single word may have the same stress pattern as a phrase or group of words.

Example: □ o □   intro**duce**   <u>rock</u> and <u>**roll**</u>

□ o o □ o   amplifi**ca**tion   <u>go</u> to the <u>**sta**</u>tion

Match the stress pattern of the numbered words with that of the phrases below. Write the matching number above each phrase.

1	after	8	modification
2	supply	9	disability
3	afterwards	10	pronunciation
4	introduce	11	confusability
5	departure	12	parapsychology
6	introduction	13	legitimization
7	biologist	14	inconceivability

6

on the table / a bird / an editor / half a pound /

sometimes I dream of it / above it / try to prevent it /

look around you / I hope they'll be coming / try some /

a lot of them / Jane's the type to manage it / help me /

far from the exit / all of them / the earth / buy an envelope /

the plane for London / under it / a bag of artichokes /

fish and chips / after the accident / a picture / the last of the apples /

the road to Manchester / a load of nonsense /

down the road to Manchester / come on Saturday

41 Word stress 5

Look at the following pairs of words and decide:

a) where the main stress is in the first word;
b) if it stays on the same syllable in the second word, or moves.

Example: The verb *support* has stress on the last syllable: ○ ☐

The noun *supporter* keeps the stress in the same place: ○ ☐ ○

The verb *concentrate* has stress on the first syllable: ☐ ○ ○

But in *concentration* the main stress moves forward: ☐ ○ ☐ ○

1	photograph	→	photography
2	estimate	→	estimation
3	consult	→	consultant
4	refer	→	referral
5	physic	→	physician
6	refuge	→	refugee
7	capable	→	capability
8	nation	→	national
9	consult	→	consultancy
10	ideal	→	idealist
11	compute	→	computer
12	astronomy	→	astronomical
13	photography	→	photographer
14	sentiment	→	sentimental
15	approve	→	approval

16	forget	→	forgettable
17	telephone	→	telephonic
18	geriatrics	→	geriatrician
19	edit	→	editor
20	picture	→	picturesque

picture   *picturesque*

 When you add an extra syllable to **two-syllable verbs** (to turn them into nouns or adjectives), the stress stays on the same syllable:

a**rrive** a**rriv**al   **cred**it **cred**itor   de**part** de**part**ure
manage **ma**nager   con**form** con**form**ist

42 Find the parenthesis

A **parenthesis** is a phrase that can be removed from the middle of a sentence without changing the main idea, and leaving the sentence still grammatical.

Example: Marilyn Monroe, **the great Hollywood star**, died in 1962.
Marilyn Monroe died in 1962.

The following sentences contain parentheses but they have no punctuation. First, read them silently, to find the parentheses. Then read them aloud. Check by listening to the recording. Careful! – some sentences contain more than one parenthesis.

1   Nick Hornby's first novel *High Fidelity* was made into a successful film.

2   Westminster Abbey just opposite the Houses of Parliament is as you probably know where every Coronation takes place.

3   The Beatles John Lennon Paul McCartney George Harrison and Ringo Starr all came from Liverpool.

4   Jane Austen 1775–1817 was the author of a number of well-loved English novels.

5   Manchester United founded in 1902 is the most successful of all British football clubs.

6   The US presidential election unfortunately was so close that it took several weeks before the winner was announced.

7   Leeds almost halfway between London and Edinburgh is a good place to break your journey north.

8   The Sydney Olympic Games it was generally felt were a great success.

9   Queen Elizabeth the elder daughter of King George VI married Philip in 1947.

---

10   Queen Elizabeth the elder daughter of King George VI married Philip son of Prince Andrew of Greece and created Duke of Edinburgh in 1947.

In **speech**, a parenthesis is marked by: a slight pause, a slight drop in pitch when the parenthesis starts, a rise at the end of the parenthesis, another slight pause, then a jump up in pitch when the main sentence starts again.

In **writing**, a parenthesis is marked by commas (as in the first example), or by brackets, or dashes:

- My sister **(the one who lives in Florida)** is visiting us next week.
  My sister is visiting us next week.

- Pronunciation – **I strongly believe** – is neglected in language teaching.
  Pronunciation is neglected in language teaching.

If the parenthesis has commas within it, use brackets or dashes to mark the parenthesis:

- Our four children – **Jo, Anna, Sam and Lisa** – all want to take part.

43 Rhythmic shift in stress

Look at the following sentences. Underline the syllable that takes the main stress in the words or phrases printed in *italic*. Check with the recording.

Examples: The performance was really *first-<u>rate</u>*.

   She runs a *<u>first</u>-rate* business

1   I always like working *outdoors*. I'm really lucky to have found an *outdoor* job.

2   Put the TV on. We'll be just in time for the *ten o'clock* news.

3   As I novelist I'd say he is *first-rate*. But he's really a *second-rate* poet.

4   My friend's *Chinese* – she plays in the *Chinese* orchestra.

5   I live in *Piccadilly*, near *Piccadilly* Circus.

6   I really hate *over-cooked* vegetables.

7   They always wear really *up-to-date* clothes.

8   You can take a boat *upstream* from Greenwich to Westminster.

9   Your food will be *stone-cold* if you don't eat it now.

10   – Haven't you heard of her? She's a really *well-known* writer.
   – She can't be that *well-known* if I haven't heard of her.

11   He's a *good-looking* guy, but not as *good-looking* as he thinks he is.

12   Really *low-paid* workers find it difficult to buy new clothes.

13   I'll only ever eat *farm-fresh* eggs but I must admit that I often buy *oven-ready* chips.

In noun and adjectival phrases, the main stress tends to come on the **second** part:

rock 'n' <u>roll</u>   *short <u>sleeves</u>*   *first-<u>class</u>*   *part-<u>time</u>*

But if such phrases are used adjectivally, in front of a noun, the stress shifts back to the **first** part (with the main stress falling on the noun):

*a <u>rock</u> 'n' roll **band**   a <u>short</u>-sleeved **shirt**   a <u>first</u>-class **ticket**   a <u>part</u>-time **job***

A similar thing happens to single words with late stress, when they are used adjectivally before a noun.

eco<u>nomic</u>   *Japa<u>nese</u>*

*<u>eco</u>nomic **mir**acle*   *<u>Japa</u>nese **bank**

---

44 Numerical expressions 1

Read the following sentences and phrases aloud, then listen to the recording to check your pronunciation.

1 Tennis: last year's champion suffered a surprise 6–0, 6–1 defeat in her opening match.

2 Manchester United 3; Arsenal 0.

3 Yesterday the European Central Bank raised borrowing rates from 3.75% to 4.25%.

4 The *Guardian*'s address is: 119 Farringdon Road, London EC1R 3ER.

5 Its phone number is 020 7278 2332.

6 And you can contact the 'Online' section at: online.feedback@guardian.co.uk

7 The company recorded a 15% drop in profits to £72.4m. Revenues were 14.5% at £863.1m.

8 CD-R machine: 750MHz Athlon processor; 12Mb SDRAM; 27Gb hard drive; 17" colour screen; 56k modem; 32Mb TN-2 graphics. Plus £1000 of software inc. Microsoft 2000 software and Supanet internet access.

9 Salary range £22,549 – £25,080 p.a. Please quote ref: MC254. Closing date for applications, 16 September.

10 The Dow Jones industrial average closed up 60.21 points at 11,252.84. The Nasdaq index finished 27.91 points ahead at 4,070.59.

The figure 0 is pronounced in different ways, according to the context. For example, it's pronounced '*love*' in tennis, '*nil*' in football, '*oh*' in telephone numbers, and '*nought*' before a decimal point.

Here are some other terms you may hear, with their written abbreviations:

six p or *six pence* = 6p	*one point seven* = 1.7
thirty pounds = £30	*megabyte* = Mb (or MB)
18 inches or *18-inch* = 18"	*gigabyte* = Gb (or GB)
dot co dot UK = .co.uk (in Internet addresses; 'Co' = 'company')	

45 Numerical expressions 2

Listen to the recording and fill in the gaps in the following sentences. Use figures and abbreviations rather than words.

Example: Today there are more than ___3,100___ Wayfare bistros, over ___400___ of them overseas, with a turnover of ___$2.2 billion___ . The company was listed on the stock exchange in ___1992___ and its market value is now ___$7 billion___ .

1   Last month my Compuserve account cost me _____ , based on a dollar fee of _____ .

2   The balance in your Direct Interest account is _____ and your cheque account is overdrawn by _____ .

3   Third-quarter results are likely to reveal a _____ net loss. This has led to the forecasted dividend being cut to just _____ , from _____ last year. This comes despite the company's decision to cut _____ jobs from its _____ -strong workforce in an attempt to reduce costs.

4   For sale: Dark blue Ford Escort _____ , under _____ miles. _____ o.n.o.

5   IBM Aptiva _____ , _____ memory. _____ hard-disk drive. _____ internal modem. Microsoft Windows _____ . Also _____ monitor.

6   The salary ranges from _____ to a maximum of _____ for a _____ -day, _____ -hour week.

7 For an application form, please phone _____ ,
quoting reference _____ .

8 Travel: There are major roadworks on the _____
between junction _____ – the _____
interchange near Orrell – and junction _____ at
Standish. A _____ speed limit is in force until
_____ .

9 Maximum temperature _____ , _____ .

10 At the New Theatre this week: *The Importance of Being Earnest.*
_____ evenings at _____ .
Matinees _____ at _____ .
Ends _____ . Seats _____ .

11 He was born in _____ and died in _____ .

12 The Hang Seng closed up _____ at _____ .
China Clay shares fell _____ to _____ despite
the company posting first-half profits of _____ yuan, up
_____ from a year ago.

13 Call _____ for the latest local and national traffic news.
Calls charged at _____ per minute.

These are some of the terms you will hear, with their written abbreviations:
miles an hour or *miles per hour* = mph
degrees Fahrenheit = °F
nine pm = 9pm (or 9 p.m.) (from Latin *post meridiem* = after noon)
nought point four per cent = 0.4%
five double six = 566
or nearest offer = o.n.o.

46 Word linking 1

A major problem of understanding spoken English is knowing where one word ends and another begins. When a word **ending** with a vowel meets a word **starting** with a vowel, they are linked either with a <w> sound or a <y> sound. (For example, *so I* may sound like so **w**hy, and *I am* may sound like *I yam*.) Identify possible <w> and <y> links in the following sequences.

Example: Why͜ʸ are you͜ʷ always in the bathroom when I need it?

1   – Now I know you'd like a cup of tea.

       – No, I really fancy a coffee for a change.

2   – I'm not going to eat this!

       – Yes, you are! Have I ever made anything you didn't like?

3   Half the oranges I bought are bad, and I had to throw away all the apples!

4   Look, it's two o'clock now. Let's meet here at three o'clock.

5   My uncle Tom lives in Scotland, and my aunt Mary in Wales. They often meet up to go on holiday in Ireland together.

6   – Has she ever been to England?

       – No, I don't think she has. But she often goes to America.

7   – That was so interesting. I didn't know any of the actors, though. Did you?

       – I knew one or two of them.

8   Now I know you said you'd be a little late. But I've been waiting here two hours! More like two and a half, in fact!

9   I'd like to return this toy I bought from you last week.

A <w> link may follow a vowel where the lips become round, as in *though I, now I, too old, to eat*.

A <y> link may follow a vowel where the lips spread, as in *see us, funny old, my own, they often* and *boy is*.

47 Word linking 2

Word linking may involve a consonant at the end of one word moving to the start of the next word. Note all examples of possible links involving consonants in the following sequences.

Examples: How long will‿it take‿us to get to the East‿End?

I'd‿really like‿a bowl‿of Italian‿ice‿cream.

1. Several of the speakers are from Africa, and one or two from America.

2. Tom's not as tall as the rest of the family.

3. We'll be there at ten o'clock, if we're at all lucky.

4. My mother lives in the USA and my mother-in-law lives in England.

5. – Where's Ann?

   – I've just left her on her own.

6. Peter and Tom must be over in the canteen, I think.

7. I'll be there in half an hour, if I can.

8. My brother and sister are over here for two and a half weeks.

9. – Where's Andrew?

   – I've just seen him buying some oranges and apples in the market.

- A consonant may move to the beginning of the next word, if this starts with a vowel sound. So *an aim* may sound like *a name*.
- The letter <r> at the end of a word corresponds (in most forms of British English) to an /r/ sound if it comes before a vowel. So *for ever* can sound like *for rever*.
- A consonant at the end of a word may move to the consonant at the start of the next word, if they go together (e.g. dr, st, cl). So *six trains* may sound like *sick strains*.
- Remember, pronunciation does not always follow spelling. For example, *one* starts with a <w> sound, not a vowel.

48 Word linking 3

Read the following text and mark the places where you think linking may take place if it is read aloud. (See Tests 46 and 47.)

Example: Peter rolled for‿ages, squeezing the‿ooze between his fingers‿and toes. As‿it dried‿it made‿his hair shoot‿into tufts. But‿it wouldn't keep still‿either, so‿it cracked‿all‿over‿and‿as‿he washed‿it‿off‿it became more‿and more slippery. But‿afterwards, his skin felt tingling and marvellous.

They lay in the warm air next to the lagoon where the water had sunk into the pits and marks made by previous creatures going to drink. The hum of insect wings filled the air. Peter felt happier than he had ever been. His mind filled with thoughts. He thought how nice it was the way Jahunda was so patient and encouraging – not like his own mother who always fussed and bothered. Scientists were always saying that dinosaurs had small brains, but they were wrong. Dinosaurs thought differently, that was all.

Jahunda's always aware of everything around, he said to himself. She senses things. She smells into the direction of the wind as if the smells were visible. [....] [She] can measure with her body; she can lift up a great big leg delicately to scratch in an exact spot behind her head. She saves her massive energy for when she needs it and doesn't crash about all the time roaring like in the films. And dinosaur tails are always made to look so stiff inside museums, when really they can move quite well. Jahunda's tail goes on for a long way behind her, but because it's thick and strong at the base and slender at the tip, she can curve it up and flick large flies from her body so expertly that they sail through the air stone-dead.

As if to illustrate his thoughts, Jahunda diverted the line of white ants which was marching single-file across her body with the touch of her tail, then gave herself a rasping scratch with a toe where they had been.

(From *Saving the Dinosaurs* by Jane Waller, Piper/Pan Macmillan, 1994)

 The /h/ sound in unstressed words such as *his* and *her* may disappear, allowing vowel linking. But ignore this for the test.

Word linking 4

Listen to the recording and see if you can fill the gaps, all of which contain various types of linking. (See Tests 46 and 47.)

Example: – What would you like __to eat__ ?

– _An ice cream_ and __some apple__ pie.

1 I'm staying with _____ of mine in Leeds.

2 _____ coming to stay with us _____ .

3 I often eat _____ with a handful _____ in the evening.

4 We walked _____ to the _____ .

5 _____ will be travelling _____ .

6 They moved from _____ to _____ .

7 They wrote _____ but _____ their _____ .

8 Could you _____ if possible?

9 They got back from holiday _____ and _____
again _____ .

10 I never expected such _____ in the middle _____ .

11 When I go out on my boat _____ forget to _____
when I land.

12 He's much _____ to _____ with a young girl like that.

13 _____ about what's going on _____ .

14 _____ do you _____ ?

15 _____ like a bite _____ before I go to bed.

16 _____ go quite _____ to _____ their little boat.

17 I'll buy you _____ .

18 _____ wanted to _____ the _____ just disappear.

19 – Is _____ somewhere?

– Yes, _____ . I've just _____ .

20 – Do you know where _____ ?

– I've just _____ in the canteen.

50 Predicting highlight shift in dialogue 2

Listen to the following conversation. You should hear a high fall on the highlighted syllables (<u>underlined</u>). (See Test 20.)

– I think I'll have a tomato sandwich.

– And **I'll** have a **cheese** sandwich. (*cheese* contrasts with *tomato*)

– A cheese **roll** for me, please. (*roll* contrasts with *sandwich*)

– And I'll have a meat pie.

– And **I'll** have a meat and po<u>ta</u>to pie. (*potato* is a new element)

Now read the following conversations. <u>Underline</u> any syllables you think will be highlighted. Then check with the recording.

1   – White coffee with sugar, please.

– Black with sugar for me, please.

– Black without sugar.

– I'll have mine white without sugar.

– Tea without sugar for me, please.

2   – OK, I'm paying. What would you like?

– That's kind of you. Steak and chips, please.

– I'd like steak and chips, too.

– Chicken and chips, please.

– Can I have a chicken curry?

– I'd prefer a fish curry.

3   – What kind of pullover are you looking for?

– Light blue, I think.

– You'd look better in dark blue, in my opinion.

– If I wanted something dark, I'd go for dark green.

– OK. A dark green pullover, then.

– I've changed my mind. I'd like a dark green shirt instead.

4   – I'd like an apple pie.

– I think I'd prefer a cherry pie.

– I'd like some cherry tart.

– I don't want anything sweet. I'll have a cheese roll.

– And I'll have a cheese sandwich.

– I've changed my mind. I'll have a cheese sandwich, too.

5   – I'm going to Oxford next week.

– Oh, I went to Oxford last week.

– What a coincidence. I went there last week, too.

– I went to Cambridge last week.

– I'm going there next week.

A highlighted syllable may be different from other syllables in the following ways:

- it may be longer
- it may be produced with greater force
- it often starts very high and falls right down to the bottom of the voice.

51 Sounding polite and friendly

Listen to the following sentences and say if the **second** speaker sounds polite and friendly or not very polite and friendly.

Example: – Mr Brown?   – My name's Smith, actually.
(1) polite and friendly   (2) not very friendly

		Polite and friendly	Not very friendly
1	– Mr Smith? – Good morning. Do come in.		
2	– Aylesbury Electricals. Can I help you? – I'd like to speak to Martin Turner, if he's available.		
3	– Where do you live in England? – I live in Wales, actually.		
4	– Do you know where the post office is? – I don't, I'm afraid.		
5	– Can I take this chair? – Sorry, somebody's sitting there, actually.		
6	– Good morning. – Ah. You're the new secretary, aren't you.		
7	– Yes? – Coffee, please.		
8	– Good morning. – Do sit down.		

To sound polite and friendly it can often help if you use a **fall-rise**.
So ↘Sit ↗down with a rise on *down* can sound more friendly than *Sit* ↘*down* with a simple fall on *down*. We often add a little tag to the end of a sentence to allow the voice to rise. If someone asks you if you know where the post office is and you reply *I* ↘*don't*, it sounds a bit impolite. But say *I* ↘*don't, I'm* ↗*afraid* and you will sound friendly. (If you don't rise on the tag it will not sound so friendly.)

52 More could be said?

Listen to the recording, and decide if the message of the **second** speaker is complete, or if he or she could say more, or is not sure.

Example: – Will the others be there too? – I believe so.
(1) message complete (2) more could be said

		Message complete	More could be said
1	– What about Jack to open the conference? – He's an excellent speaker.		
2	– Are you ready? – I think so.		
3	– Well, that's what I have in mind. – I see what you mean.		
4	– She's always well prepared for meetings. – That's true.		
5	– Was it a good weekend? – Saturday was fine.		
6	– Do you always understand him? – Generally.		
7	– The matter is very urgent. – I fully appreciate that.		
8	– Do you see what I'm getting at? – I agree with you, up to a point.		

Sometimes the use of a **fall-rise** instead of a **fall** means that something more could be said. If someone asks *Did you like the film?* and you answer ↘Yes, then there is nothing more you need say; but if you answer ↗Yes, with a fall-rise, then it is clear that you are not sure and could go on to say more about it.

53 Double trouble

In English we love 'double' words or phrases such as:

flip-flop	(where just the vowel is changed)
head over heels	(where the two main words start with the same sound)
pay day	(where both parts rhyme)

It's pay day!

A See if you can make words or phrases by linking an item from side A with another from side B.

A	B
back / band / chit- / chock-a- / ding / doom and / fight or / fly- / hale and / helter- / hey / higgledy- / hip / hoi / hoo- / hurdy / hurly- / knick- / like it or / mish / namby- / pell- / pic / ping / pitter- / riff- / see / ship / teeny / tick / tip / tit / willy- /	bit / block / burly / by / chat / day / dong / flight / gloom / gurdy / ha / hearty / hop / knack / lump it / mash / mell / nic / nilly / pack / pamby / patter / piggledy / polloi / pong / raff / saw / shape / skelter / stand / tock / top / weeny /

B   Now decide which of the double expressions fit in the sentences below.

a   Their living-room is really crowded. Every surface is
_____ with _____ s.

b   Most of the meeting was wasted in _____ . No
progress was made at all.

c   In cheap supermarkets the goods are often laid out all
_____ .

d   They have no choice. They'll have to accept it
_____ .

e   During her _____ she toured Europe and the USA
every year.

f   The financial markets are very nervous. It's all
_____ at the moment.

g   My father-in-law, at ninety, is looking really
_____ .

My father-in-law, at ninety...

54 Sounds maze

Hidden in the maze are a lot of English first names, including shortened forms (*Nick* is short for *Nicholas*). They may be horizontal (→ only), vertical (↓ only) or diagonal (↘,↖,↙or↗).

Examples: dʒæk = Jack   nɪk = Nick

w	ŋ	dʒ	æ	k	f	æ	n	i	n
m	eɪ	æ	n	t	ə	n	i	ɪ	æ
n	iː	n	ə	r	l	s	k	e	n
ɔː	ɒ	ɪ	aɪ	r	ɪ	tʃ	ə	d	dʒ
m	ʌ	s	ɑː	uː	s	æ	l	i	ə
ə	p	tʃ	əʊ	θ	ə	n	ə	əʊ	l
n	ɔː	m	ə	f	t	e	s	ə	ə
p	l	t	ɒ	m	i	d	e	t	d
t	iː	n	ə	æ	ɪ	dʒ	eɪ	k	ɪ
v	ə	r	ɒ	n	ɪ	k	ə	v	ɒ

Here are the names, including one that does not appear in the maze: Angela, Ann/Anne, Anna, Annie/Anny, Anthony, Dave, Ed, Eddy, Fanny, Felicity, Jack, Jake, Jane, Janice, Kate, Ken, Kim, Mick, Nicholas, Nick, Nina, Norma, Norman, Paul, Richard, Ruth, Sally, Sophie, Tessa, Tina, Tommy, Veronica, Wayne

55 Using phonemic script 3

Here are some words and phrases written in phonemic script. Transcribe them into ordinary script, then decide where they fit into the text below.

a	sɔːt ə 'pɜːsən	**g**	'wʌndəfəl pleɪs	**m**	ðeɪv gɒt ɪt
b	reɪn	**h**	'eksələm 'mɑːkɪts	**n**	'mɑːvələs
c	'stəʊni	**i**	gəʊ ʷɪn ðə siː	**o**	'iːvəm 'betər
d	braʊn suːp	**j**	'ɑːkɪtektʃəz naɪs	**p**	briːz
e	'muːvɪŋ	**k**	'kʌp‚praɪs	**q**	'hɒlədeɪz
f	wemp bʌst	**l**	fən'tæstɪk(ə)li		

Jack and I were going to Italy for our __holidays__ , but the

1 _____ travel firm that was offering three weeks in the sun

for £500 2 _____ . We went to Brighton instead. Now

Brighton is a 3 _____ to have a seaside holiday,

provided you don't want to 4 _____ or lie on the

beach. The beach is 5 _____ , you see, and the sea is a cold,

6 _____ . But the restaurants in Brighton are

7 _____ good. Indian, Chinese, you name it,

8 _____ . There are theatres and cinemas and some

really 9 _____ . Even the 10 _____ .

You can have a 11 _____ holiday in Brighton. And it's

12 _____ if you're the 13 _____ who

likes a constant stiff 14 _____ , fast- 15 _____ clouds,

and a good chance of 16 _____ .

The transcription includes examples of elision, assimilation and linking. (See Tests 15, 16, 46 and 47.)

56 Sounds crossword

This is like a standard crossword, but all the words must be written in phonemic script.

1 k	r	2 iː	3 m	■	4	5		6	7
r	■	8					■	9	
ɪ	■	10		■		■	11		
12 s				■	13	14	■		■
m	■	■		■	15				■
16 ə	17	18			■		■		19
20 s			■	21	22		23		
■	24					■		■	
■		■		■	■			■	
25			■	■	26			■	

Across

1 Good in coffee.
4 You find them in classrooms and offices.
8 The game played at Wimbledon.
9 We looked for it high and _____ .
10 Pronoun.
11 It sounds as if it could be below your ankle; or what a doctor can do.
12 Someone who makes music with his or her voice.
13 *I am*: shorter than usual.
15 Comparatively neat.
16 Her mother _____ her to stay up late.
20 What you do in a chair.
21 Another word for trade and commerce.
24 Sounds like *sport*, if you say it fast.
25 _____ is _____ and west is west.
26 Opposite of *quiet*.

Down

1 Winter festival.
2 _____ and drinking.
3 Copper, bronze and iron, for example.
4 Holy.
5 The sound of the letter before T.
6 Not at all dirty, comparatively.
7 It could be under your foot; or it could survive after you are dead.
14 Breakfast, lunch, and dinner are all _____ .
17 People make these before they go shopping.
18 Opposite of *inner*.
19 By midnight I am usually _____ .
21 *Buy* in the past.
22 Same as 10 across.
23 He took a hammer and _____ down the lid.

57 Find the rhymes 3

Here are some more very short, two-line poems, but the rhyming words are missing. Try to guess the missing words which complete each poem. If you can't think of any, choose them from the list. (The list contains some words which rhyme, but which do not make sense in the poems.)

1   'I think the _____

    Would like to _____ '

2   'It might make _____

    To build a _____ '

3   'My youngest _____

    Sure likes to _____ '

4 'I'll try to _____

To get a _____'

5 'He's too _____

To want to _____'

alone / aunts / bone / box / dames / dance / fence / fight / friendly /
fun / girls / loan / lone / none / one / pence / phone / polite / right /
run / scared / sense / sight / son / sun / trance

58 Pronunciation of 'chunks'

'Chunks' of language are groups of words that belong together. Chunks are fixed – the **words** are a fixed group, and the **pronunciation** is usually fixed too, especially the stress and intonation.

Examples: *fish and chips* *rock 'n' roll*
raining cats and dogs *How do you do?*

Read the following. How do you think the chunks (in *italics*) will be spoken? Check with the recording.

1 – Teenagers! I never know when Mark's going to get home.
– *Tell me about it.* (informal = 'You don't have to tell me. I know.')

2 – When I win the lottery, I'll buy a luxury boat.
– *You wish!* (informal = 'You don't have a chance.')

3 – Would you like to go out with me?
– *In your dreams!* (informal = 'You may want that, but it's not going to happen.')

4 – Do we have a chance of winning?
– *No way!* (informal = 'Definitely not.')

5 – What do you think they're going to do?
– Well, *as far as I'm concerned* they can do what they want.

6 – What are you going to study when you get to university?
– *As if!* (informal = 'That's unlikely.')

7 – What would you do if you won the lottery?
– *I should be so lucky!* (informal = 'That would be great, but it will never happen.')

8 – Do you see any solution?
– Well, *in my opinion* they should build more roads.

9 – I'm sure the next President will be a woman.
– *Yeah, right.* (very informal = 'not a chance')

10 – Have you read about these teachers being attacked in schools?
– *Call me old-fashioned*, but I think there should be much stricter discipline. ('I know this is rather an old-fashioned thing to say.')

11 – What do you think should be our first priority?
  – Well, *off the top of my head*, I'd say we have to concentrate on reducing the cost of raw materials. ('I haven't had much chance to think about it.')

12 – *What on earth* do you think you're doing?
  – *Mind your own business.*

13 – I plan on starting up my own dot.com company next year.
  – *That's easier said than done.*

14 – Have you seen the way she does her hair?
  – Well, *live and let live, that's what I always say.*

15 – Did you hear about Joe? He got promoted last month; and he won the lottery on Saturday!
  – *It's all right for some.*

16 – Could you lend me £50 till Friday?
  – *Are you out of your mind?* After last time?

17 – What do you think I should do with my winnings? Open a savings account, or buy shares?
  – *It's six of one, half a dozen of the other.* But, *to be on the safe side*, I'd put half the money in the bank.

18 – What's Lucy's husband called?
  – *Wait a minute.* Oh, um, *it's on the tip of my tongue.*

19 – Ah, look at the little darling!
  – Yes, and she's *as good as gold*; never a sound out of her.

20 – Can I speak to Ann Todd, please?
  – She's not in today. *Would you like to leave a message?*

21 – Hello, Tom! *How's tricks?* (informal = 'How are you?')
  – Hello, Joe! *Haven't seen you for ages!*

22 – Well, I think we should all stay later in the evening.
  – *Speak for yourself.* ('That's your opinion, but I disagree.')

59 Did it happen?

Sometimes the choice between a **fall-rise** and a **fall** can completely change the meaning of a message. Listen carefully to these examples (noting the change of tonic syllables).

Examples:

    a) I hoped ⌄Jane would be coming.   (= she **didn't** come)

    b) I ⌄hoped Jane would be ↗coming.   (= she **did** come)

Now listen to the recordings and decide what is meant.

1   They told us we would get in free!

    a) = we did get in free

    b) = we had to pay to get in

2   I thought it would rain today.

    a) = it didn't rain

    b) = it did rain

3   The bus didn't stop because you waved your hand.

    a) = it didn't stop

    b) = it stopped, but not because you waved your hand

4   It's about time they invited us to dinner.

    a) = they haven't invited us yet, but they should

    b) = they have finally invited us

5   He wasn't given the job because of his Mafia connections.

    a) = his Mafia connections were the reason why he wasn't given the job

    b) = he was given the job, but not because of his Mafia connections

6 It's about time Peter was given a better job.

a) = he has finally been given a better job

b) = he should be given a better job

7 They told us the museum was great.

a) = it was great

b) = it wasn't great

8 I thought Mary would win.

a) = Mary won

b) = Mary didn't win

9 It's about time Tom got a good job.

a) = Tom has finally got a good job.

b) = other people are getting good jobs, but not Tom

10 I hoped we would win more gold medals this time.

a) = we did win more medals

b) = we didn't win more medals

 See page v for tonic syllables. See Tests 51 and 52 for more on fall-rise intonation.

60 wɒtʃə seɪ ?

It can be a shock the first time you hear how fast English is spoken by native speakers (especially among themselves). For example, the question *What did you say?* can become wɒtʃə seɪ (which sounds like *watcher say?*).

A Match the following common phrases with their equivalents in phonemic script. Then check the recording.

1	*Do you want a cup of tea?*	a	fænsijə baɪ twiːt
2	*You must be joking!*	b	gɒtəni tʃeɪndʒ
3	*Come off it!*	c	gɒtə gəʊ twɜːk
4	*Shut up!*	d	dʒə wʌnə kʌpə tiː
5	*I'm worn out.*	e	aɪ mɒf tə bed
6	*Fancy a bite to eat?*	f	kʌ mɒfɪt
7	*I'm off to bed.*	g	ʃʌ tʌp
8	*Got any change?*	h	kənjə lemijə kwɪd
9	*Got to go to work.*	i	jə mʌs bi dʒəʊkɪŋ
10	*Can you lend me a quid?*	j	aɪm wɔː naʊt

B Now work out the following questions and responses from their transcription.

1	(Q) wɒtsjə neɪm ?	(R) fəgɒtə nɔːredi ?
2	(Q) weədʒə kʌm frɒm ?	(R) frə mɪtəlijə njuː ?
3	(Q) fænsijə kɒfi ?	(R) nɒt dʒʌ snaʊ, θæŋks
4	(Q) jə wɒf naʊ ?	(R) həʊl dɒnə sek
5	(Q) gɒt ðə taɪm ?	(R) tem pɑː stuː

Vocabulary notes
Come off it! = you can't be serious / you must be joking
quid = pound (£) (in British English)

Answers

Test 1

1 c, a, b, d	6 a, c, b, d	11 a, d, c, b
2 d, a, c, b	7 d, c, a, b	12 a, b, d, c
3 b, a, c, d	8 a, b, d, c	13 d, a, c, b
4 c, d, a, b	9 a, c, d, b	14 c, b, d, a
5 b, a, d, c	10 a, b, c, d	

Test 2

1c / 2a / 3c / 4a / 5a / 6d / 7c / 8b / 9a / 10b / 11a / 12a / 13a / 14d / 15b

Test 3

1 (a) to (b) for (c) an
2 (a) I've/I have (b) from
3 (a) must've / must have (b) to the
4 (a) I'd / I would (b) a (c) or (d) of
5 (a) for (b) them to
6 (a) Do you (b) where
7 (a) her (b) was (c) her (d) to
8 (a) I'd been / I had been
  (b) I'd have / I would have (c) to
9 (a) where there were

Test 4

1 = two	5 = zero	9 = one	13 = one
2 = one	6 = three	10 = five	14 = three
3 = four	7 = two	11 = one	15 = two
4 = one	8 = one	12 = three	16 = one

Remember it is the **sounds**, not the **letters**, which count, which means that *Tom* has a different vowel from the first syllable of *tomato* (which is unstressed and contains schwa).

Test 5

A

1	*circle*	starts with /s/, the others with /k/
2	*these*	starts with /ð/, the others with /θ/
3	*whose*	starts with /h/, the others with /w/
4	*choir*	starts with /kw/, the others with /tʃ/
5	*pneumatic*	starts with /n/, the others with /p/
6	*moon*	starts with /m/, the others with /n/

B

1	*rubbed*	ends with /d/, the others with /t/
2	*dropped*	ends with /t/, the others with /d/
3	*of*	ends with /v/, the others with /f/
4	*begs*	ends with /z/, the others with /s/
5	*lump*	ends with /p/, the others with /m/
6	*arch*	ends with /tʃ/, the others with /k/

Test 6

A

1	*robbed*	ends with /d/, the others with /t/
2	*shaped*	ends with /t/, the others with /ɪd/
3	*shops*	ends with /s/, the others with /z/
4	*names*	ends with /z/, the others with /ɪz/
5	*faded*	ends with /ɪd/, the others with /t/
6	*wicked*	ends with /ɪd/, the others with /t/

Note that *wicked* is an adjective, not a past participle, and has an unusual pronunciation.

B
1 *on*   contains the vowel /ɒ/, the others /ʌ/
2 *leak*   contains the vowel /iː/, the others /eɪ/
3 *waste* contains the vowel /eɪ/, the others /æ/
4 *have*   contains the vowel /æ/, the others /eɪ/
5 *fool*   contains the vowel /uː/, the others /ʊ/
6 *loud*   contains the vowel /aʊ/, the others /uː/
7 *give*   contains the vowel /ɪ/, the others /aɪ/
8 *must*   contains the vowel /ʌ/, the others /uː/

Test 7

A

1 three, except *chocolate* (two)
2 one, except *wanted* (two)
3 two, except *Manchester* (three)

4 four, except *banana* (three)
5 two, except *through* (one)

B

1 o□o   except *politics*   = □o o
2 o□   except *prostate*   = □o
3 □o   except *refer*   = o□

4 □o   except *submit*   = o□
5 o□o   except *Angela*   = □o o

Test 8

Short	Long
Sammy Cathy Tammy	Dean Jane David
Becky Beth Ted	Pete Jean Sheila Mike
Mick Timmy Bill	Simon Rose Joan
Ross Tom Bonnie	Luke Susan Muriel
Patty Bud	Martha Bert Mary

Test 9

o□   *RePEAT, surPRISE, beLOW, aBOVE, postPONE, aLLOW, coLLECT, forGIVE, beLIEVE, preFER*
Note that most of these are two-syllable **verbs**, which usually start with a very weak syllable.
The two prepositions have a similar pattern to verbs. Compare *aBOVE / aLLOW* and *beLOW / beLIEVE*.

□o   *EDit, TEACHer, MANage, BOTTle, LISten, UNder, ROYal, LIMit, VANish, PICture, FUNny, VILlage, SWEEten, COVer, AFter, LUCKy, FORmer, LOcal*
Note that these must have front stress, because they end with a syllable which is normally weak:
• schwa (*teacher, under, picture, cover, after, former*)
• short /i/ (*lucky, funny*)
• syllabic /l/ (*bottle, local, royal*)
• syllabic /n/ (*listen, sweeten*)
• <-age> (*manage, village*)
• <-it> (*edit, limit*)
• <-ish> (*vanish*)

Test 10

Always □o	Always o□	□o when it is a noun o□ when it is a verb
varnish/damage/answer/ credit/fiddle/treasure	repeat/escape/debate/ regret/reply/account	subject/contrast/rebel/rewrite/ increase/present/object/export/ suspect/replay/produce/pervert

Test 11

1 weak	4 strong	7 strong, weak
2 strong	5 weak, strong	8 weak
3 strong	6 weak, strong	9 strong

Test 12

1 A OK, that's two white ↘coffees.
   B No, I always drink ↘BLACK coffee.
2 A So, your daughter sells ↘clothes.
   B No, my daughter ↘MAKES clothes.
3 A I used to live in the South of ↘France, like ↘you.
   B No, I used to live in the South of ↘ITaly.
4 A Would you like some potato soup for lunch later on?
   B I'd prefer ↘FISH soup, if that's okay.
5 A You're a com↘puter operator, I understand.
   B No, I'm a computer ↘PROgrammer.
6 A Did you buy that cotton shirt you were looking at?
   B No, I bought a ↘SILK shirt in↘stead.
7 A Would you like to sit outside?
   B I'd prefer to sit ↘INside, if possible.
8 A Do you fancy fish and ↘chips?
   B I'd rather have ↘CHIcken and chips.
9 A So your mother's ↘Welsh.
   B No, my ↘FAther's Welsh.
10 A Let's meet at half past ↘ten.
    B I'd rather meet at ↘QUARter past ten.
11 A So your partner is John ↘Smith.
    B No, my partner is ↘JANE Smith.
12 A So your son's going to play for Manchester ↘City.
    B No, he's going to play for Manchester U↘NIted.
13 A So your son's going to play for Leeds U↘nited.
    B No, he's going to play for ↘MANchester United.
14 A Let's meet at quarter past ↘nine.
    B I think we'd better meet at quarter ↘TO nine.

Test 13

1c / 2d / 3b / 4a / 5a / 6c / 7d / 8b

Test 14

1 ↘I've got ↘ONE ↗sister, and my ∪wife has ↘TWO sisters.
2 I didn't say we'd meet at quarter ↘TO ↗six, I said quarter ↘PAST six!
3 My ↘sis↗ter was born in nineteen ↘FIFty-↗nine, and my ∪wife in nineteen ↘SIXty-nine.
4 ↘Joe lives in ↘NORTH A↗merica, and ↘Pab↗lo in ↘SOUTH America.
5 ↘DIEsel ↗engines cause more pollution than ↘PETrol engines.
6 I've ↘never been to South A↘MERi↗ca, but I ↘have been to South ↘AFrica.
7 My ↘grandfather was born in nineteen-o-∪ FOUR; and my grand↘MOTH↗er was born in nineteen-o-↘FIVE.
8 He served not only in the ↘FIRST World ↗War, but also in the ↘SECond World War.
9 Don't let's go on the twenty-∪ FIRST; let's make it the twenty-↘EIGHTH.
10 I don't live in the ↘OUTskirts of ↗London; I live right in the ↘CENtre of London.

Test 15
1 lan(d)lady ... han(d)bag
2 firs(t) girl ... earn(ed) twenty poun(d)s
3 secon(d) boy
4 don('t) know ... finish(ed) work
5 don('t) like ... fas(t) food
6 perfec(t)ly
7 han(d)s
8 I watch(ed) ... las(t) night

Test 16

No.	Word(s)	Slow version	Fast version
1	in place	ɪn pleɪs	ɪm pleɪs
	in case	ɪn keɪs	ɪŋ keɪs
2	Green Park	griːn pɑːk	griːm pɑːk
	Hyde Park	haɪd pɑːk	haɪb pɑːk
3	third person	θɜːd pɜːsən	θɜːb pɜːsən
	red coat	red kəʊt	reg kəʊt
4	and bacon	ənd beɪkən	əm beɪkən
	and mashed	ənd mæʃt	əm mæʃ
5	in Paris	ɪn pærɪs	ɪm pærɪs
	in Berlin	ɪn bɜːlɪn	ɪm bɜːlɪn
6	handbag	hændbæg	hæmbæg
	handkerchief*	hæŋkətʃiːf	hæŋkətʃɪf

* Elision and assimilation have changed the pronunciation of *handkerchief* permanently.

Test 17

1 mist patches
2 prime minister
3 bad guys
4 next train
5 wouldn't choose (or wouldn't use)
6 lettuce salad
7 clothes
8 land mine
9 six students
10 sun bed
11 handcuffs
12 cold storage
13 fast food
14 cat person
15 World Cup
16 face the facts
17 cold feet
18 mind the gap
19 guest list
20 not guilty
21 six quid = £6
22 eight girls, eight boys
23 fast speech

Test 18
1a / 2a / 3b / 4a / 5b / 6a / 7a / 8b / 9b

Test 19
Short vowel sounds

pit pɪt	**pat** pæt	**pet** pet	**putt** pʌt	**pot** pɒt	**put** pʊt
rich	flashed	death	month	shone	would
still	banned	hemmed	just	dock	hood
bin	rang	next	love	don	wood
ridge	hat	breath	ton	cloth	should
link	stabbed	said	son	cough	could
hymn	cab	edge	blood	dog	foot
itch	black	begged	monk	shopped	stood

Long vowel sounds

peat piːt	**pert** pɜːt	**part** pɑːt	**port** pɔːt	**boot** buːt
breathe	curl	cart	lawn	suit
scene	herd	farm	poured	loom
creep	earn	calm	torn	cruise
piece	bird	arch	floor	hoop
feast	germ	palm	sword	hoot
eve	purr	barred	ought	move
leaf	pearl	bard	chalk	soup

Test 20

1

– Where did you put the **potatoes**?
– Where do you **think** I put the potatoes? There's only **one** place **to** put them!
– Well, **I** can't find them!
– They're in the **cupboard**.
– But I've **looked** in the cupboard.
– You **can't** have looked in the cupboard.
– Well, I **have**.
– **Sorry** … They're still in the **shopping** bag.

2

– Where are you spending your **holidays**?
– In **France**.
– **Where** in France?
– The **south**.
– I've never been to the south of **France**. But I've lived in the south of **Spain**.
– Where **exactly** in the south?
– In **Seville**.
– That's a **coincidence**. My **daughter** lives in Seville!
– **Which** of your daughters?
– **Susan**, my **eldest** daughter.
– What's she **doing** there?
– Working as a **teacher**. An **English** teacher.

Test 21

Phrases	Compound nouns	
cotton shirts	shopping centre	cotton factory
Buckingham Palace	car keys	steel mills
Cambridge Avenue	handbag	orange juice
South America	White House	
cheese sandwich	High Street	

Test 22

1 I **al**ways **vis**it my **par**ents in the **sum**mer.
2 Do you **fan**cy a **cup** of **cof**fee?
3 My **aunt** and **un**cle **live** in the **North** of **Eng**land.
4 Re**mind** me to **pick** the **chil**dren **up** from **school** at **four** o'**clock**.
5 I **don't know John** Smith, but I **know** his **sis**ter **Jane** Smith.
6 I **think** we'll **eat** in the **din**ing-**room**, for a **change**.
7 I'd **like** to **speak** to **Thom**as, if he's **in**.
8 **Su**sie sug**gest**ed we **meet** at the **sta**tion.
9 **Con**rad com**posed** a con**cer**to for **trum**pet!
10 **What's** that **shirt** made **of**?

Test 23

/iːn/	/eɪn/	/eɪt/	/ɔː/	/aɪn/
seen	main	hate	law	wine
bean	complain	gate	core	design
between	insane	relate	four	pine
convene	pane	state	raw	refine
mean	refrain	wait	roar	resign
scene	reign	weight	shore	sign

/ænd/	/ɜːt/	/ɜːl/	/ɔːk/	/aɪt/
band	dirt	girl	fork	white
canned	alert	earl	cork	delight
hand	curt	furl	hawk	height
land	hurt	hurl	stalk	incite
spanned	pert	pearl	stork	kite
tanned	shirt	whirl	walk	polite

Test 24

/əʊn/	/uː/	/ɜː/	/ɔːt/	/iːst/
phone	who	sir	court	east
atone	chew	confer	caught	beast
loan	flu	demur	fort	ceased
lone	threw	fir	fought	least
mown	through	fur	snort	pieced
sewn	too	purr	taught	yeast

/ɜːk/	/eɪk/	/ɪst/	/ækt/	/ɒft/
work	make	mist	pact	soft
jerk	break	gist	act	aloft
perk	opaque	hissed	retract	coughed
shirk	quake	insist	sacked	doffed
smirk	shake	kissed	tracked	loft
Turk	steak	list	whacked	waft

Test 25

/ɜːd/	/ɔːd/	/ɑːm/	/ɑːd/	/eɪd/
word	board	farm	card	shade
bird	horde	alarm	charred	conveyed
curd	pawed	balm	hard	displayed
heard	poured	calm	lard	maid
herd	snored	charm	sparred	parade
spurred	flawed	psalm	starred	weighed

/æks/	/ɜːm/	/uːn/	/uːm/	/ɔːs/
axe	germ	June	loom	Morse
backs	firm	loon	boom	course
fax	perm	noon	gloom	force
relax	squirm	prune	groom	gorse
sacks	term	strewn	tomb	hoarse
shacks	worm	tune	womb	sauce

Test 26

A

1	**droop**	(loop / stoop / snoop / coop)
2	**mash**	(cash / dash / lash / smash / bash)
3	**make**	(bake / cake / fake / hake / shake / lake)
4	**moon**	(soon / noon / loon / spoon / boon)
5	**stitch**	(itch / snitch / witch / pitch / hitch)
6	**chest**	(best / nest / pest / behest / vest / west)
7	**bond**	(fond / pond / blonde / beyond / Honda / Rhonda)
8	**mud**	(dud / thud / spud / bud)
9	**file**	(Nile / mile / pile / rile / bile / smile)
10	**taste**	(paste / haste / chaste / baste)
11	**squirm**	(squirt / firm / skirt / skirmish / quirk) i.e < i > + < r > + consonant
12	**loom**	(doom / gloom / groom / boom)

B

1	**cut**	(rut / hut / but / shut / nut / gut)
2	**charm**	(farm / alarm / harm)
3	**storm**	(norm / form / gormless / dormitory)
4	**boot**	(coot / loot / hoot / shoot / root)
5	**fear**	(dear / near / rear / clear / gear / shear / spear)
6	**cork**	(stork / pork / fork)
7	**dart**	(art / part / start / cart / smart)
8	**maid**	(paid / laid / raid / staid)
9	**call**	(ball / all / gall / hall / stall / appall / fall)
10	**lord**	(cord / chord / order / sword / border)
11	**dome**	(home / Rome / tome / gnome)
12	**pant**	(cant / rant / phantom / ant)

Test 27

A

1	scramble	7	rage	13	crack
2	mutter	8	adder	14	pang
3	bun	9	spud	15	mock
4	flan	10	splash	16	gloom
5	loop	11	Cupid		
6	dray	12	juke		

Test 28

1	calm / farm	4	heard / word
2	ought / court	5	speak / week
3	bite / night		

Test 29

B

1 departure / musician / banana / potato / computer / survival / productive
2 editor / afterwards / seasickness / customer / luckily / chemistry / activate
3 refugee / interfere / mistranslate / overpaid
4 ultimatum / journalistic / existential / California / indecision / avocado
5 survivable / commemorate / expandable / executive
6 oceanographer / conductivity / inexcusable / productivity / exhibitionist
7 hallucination / determination / investigation / congratulations

Test 30
1 bought / short
2 take / steak
3 play / day

4 late / weight
5 boys / noise

Test 31
balls, bawls / bear, bare / bold, bowled / cue, queue / ducked, duct /
fort, fought / grate, great / hair, hare / hold, holed / missed, mist / air, heir /
packed, pact / pair, pear / past, passed / peace, piece / pleas, please / pore, pour /
seam, seem / shake, sheikh / side, sighed / sight, site / slay, sleigh / stake, steak /
stalk, stork / weak, week / weakly, weekly / wade, weighed / wear, where /
whine, wine

Test 32
aisle, I'll, isle / bard, barred / beer, bier / board, bored / caught, court /
cawed, cored, chord / died, dyed / dire, dyer / doe, dough / flawed, floored /
knew, new / heard, herd / he'll, heal, heel / lacks, lax / mail, male /
maize, maze / might, mite / knight, night / knit, nit / pail, pale /
pare, pair, pear / rain, reign / saw, soar, sore / seam, seem / slay, sleigh /
stare, stair / teas, tees, tease / toad, toed, towed / wait, weight / we'll, wheel

Test 33
– Lousy **weather** we've been having recently.

– We haven't been having much **sun**, that's for **sure**. I got **caught** in the **rain** this **morning** and got wet **through**.

– Me **too**. And how about that cold **mist** first thing? I went out **bare**-headed to get **some** fire-**wood** and haven't **been** warm since. And my hands got quite **sore** as well. Really **raw**, they feel.

– I **know what you** mean. I always get aches and **pains** in the winter. Anyway, **we're** off to get some **sun next week**. **We've** booked a few **days** in **Singapore**.

– Yes, I **heard** you had. Lucky **you**! Still, I shouldn't **moan**. We **flew** to Florida **last year, which** was really nice, and it's only **four** weeks till we visit my **son** and daughter-in-**law** in **Rome**. Haven't **seen** them **for ages**. We only **made** the booking yesterday, **through** the internet. Mary's already **packed**; she can't **wait**.

– Well, tell her she won't **need** her **fur** coat any**way**.

– **Right. OK. I'll see** you later.

– **Bye. See you around.**

Test 34
We live in an old **red brick** house in Sussex. The **weather's** been really **hot** the last month or so. In fact we've never known such **summer heat**. Most mornings there's a **light mist** at first, but that clears away quickly, leaving a fine **sunny day**. But some mornings have started with a **dense fog**.

Anyway, when I **woke up** this **morning** I was expecting another lovely **hot summer day**. But when I looked outside I saw that it was **pouring** with **rain**, and it felt so cold that I decided to **light** a **fire**. Then I spent a happy twenty minutes in the bath **reading** a **book**. My **wife Lyn** prefers to **take** a **shower**, but I always like to **soak** in a hot **tub**.

After breakfast **I poured** myself a final **cup** of coffee, then settled back to **read** yesterday's **mail**, which I'd been too busy to deal with. There was a **whole stack** of **junk mail**, as usual, but I was pleased to **get a postcard** from my **mum** and **dad**, who were spending a few **days** in **Rome**.

It was **time** to get **ready** for church, so I put on my best **suit** and **tie** with black **shoes** and **socks** while Lyn decided to wear the **frilly** pink **suit** she'd bought at the Harrods' sale.

Unfortunately, when I tried to **start** the **car** I found that I had a **flat battery**. Luckily my next **door** neighbour **Penny** helped me out, and we were soon on the road.

Test 35

London / Beijing / Paris
Rome / Tokyo / Manchester
Lima / Helsinki / New York
Cardiff / Berlin / Belgrade

Madrid / Brighton / Warsaw
Washington / Bath / Los Angeles
Quito / Seoul / Venice

Test 36

prɑːg / ˈlɪzbən / ˈdʌblɪn
ˈbrʌsəlz / ˈhʌŋg(ə)ri / ˈmɒskəʊ
ˈhæmbɜːg / dʒəˈniːvə / dʒəˈpæn
brəˈzɪl / ˈtaɪlænd (or) ˈtaɪlənd / ˈdʒɜːməni
weɪlz / ˈɪŋglənd / ˈskɒtlənd
bæŋˈkɒk / ˈɪt(ə)li / kəˈriːə (or) kɒˈriːə
ˈtʃaɪnə / məˈnɪlə / ˌæm(p)stəˈdæm (or) ˈæm(p)stədæm
dʒəˈkɑːtə / griːs / ˈtɜːki

Test 37
Picture 1

b) No, it's sitting on the **KIT**chen table.
c) No, it's **SITT**ing on the kitchen table.
d) No, it's sitting **ON** the kitchen table.

Picture 2

a) No, she's **YOUNG**er than the boy.
b) No, he's **STAND**ing at the table.
c) No, she's sitting at the table **EAT**ing.
d) No, he has a **PLATE** in his hand.

Picture 3

a) No, she's wearing a **LONG** skirt.
b) No, he's **SHORT**er than the woman.
c) No, she's wearing a long **SKIRT**.
d) No, he's wearing a **SHIRT** and jeans.

Picture 4

a) No, there are **TWO** cars in the garage.
b) No, it's a **THREE**-storey house.
c) No, they're **IN** the garage.
d) No, she's looking out of the **WIN**dow.

Test 38

1 Not the **GREEKS**; the **RO**mans.
2 Not the **EIGH**teen fifties; the **NINE**teen fifties.
3 Not sixteen **SEV**enty-six; sixteen **SIX**ty-six.
4 Not a **CLOTHES** shop; a **TOY** shop.
5 Not Oxford **ROAD**; Oxford **CIR**cus.
6 Not the **EAST** End; the **WEST** End.
7 Not near **WEST**minster Bridge; near Water**LOO** Bridge.
8 Not the **NA**tional Festival Hall; the **RO**yal Festival Hall.
9 Not **WEST**; **EAST**.
10 Not a **RAIL**way station; a **PO**wer station.

Test 39

1 all /ɜːt/ except *Bart* /ɑːt/
2 all /uːt/ except *soot* /ʊt/
3 all /eɪt/ except *height* /aɪt/
4 all /ʊk/ except *spook* /uːk/
5 all /uːd/ except *good* /ʊd/
6 all /uːd/ except *sewed* /əʊd/
7 all /ɜːk/ except *clerk* /ɑːk/
8 all /ækt/ except *baked* /eɪkt/
9 all /iːn/ except *sign* /aɪn/
10 all /eɪz/ except *size* /aɪz/
11 all /iːk/ except *steak* /eɪk/
12 all /ʊt/ except *cut* /ʌt/
13 all /aɪt/ except *weight* /eɪt/
14 all /ɔːk/ except *work* /ɜːk/
15 all /aɪt/ except *lied* /aɪd/
16 all /eə/ except *clear* /ɪə/
17 all /ɑːd/ except *bared* /eəd/
18 all /uːk/ except *look* /ʊk/
19 all /ɔːt/ except *coughed* /ɒft/
20 all /ɪst/ except *prised* /aɪzd/

Test 40

1 after — try some / help me
2 supply — a bird / the earth
3 afterwards — all of them / under it
4 introduce — half a pound / fish and chips
5 departure — above it / a picture
6 introduction — look around you / on the table
7 biologist — a lot of them / an editor
8 modification — try to prevent it / far from the exit
9 disability — buy an envelope / come on Saturday
10 pronunciation — a load of nonsense / the plane for London
11 confusability — the road to Manchester / a bag of artichokes
12 parapsychology — after the accident / sometimes I dream of it
13 legitimization — the last of the apples / I hope they'll be coming
14 inconceivability — down the road to Manchester / Jane's the type to manage it

Test 41

1	photograph / photography	*moves from* ☐ o o	*to*	o ☐ o o
2	estimate / estimation	*moves from* ☐ o o	*to*	☐ o ☐ o
3	consult / consultant	*no change* o ☐		o ☐ o
4	refer / referral	*no change* o ☐		o ☐ o
5	physic / physician	*moves from* ☐ o	*to*	o ☐ o
6	refuge / refugee	*moves from* ☐ o	*to*	☐ o ☐
7	capable / capability	*moves from* ☐ o o	*to*	☐ o ☐ o o
8	nation / national	*no change* ☐ o		☐ o o
9	consult / consultancy	*no change* o ☐		o ☐ o o
10	ideal / idealist	*no change* o ☐		o ☐ o
11	compute / computer	*no change* o ☐		o ☐ o
12	astronomy / astronomical	*moves from* o ☐ o o	*to*	☐ o ☐ o o
13	photography / photographer	*no change* o ☐ o o		o ☐ o o

14	sentiment / sentimental	*moves from*	□ ○ ○	*to*	□ ○ □ ○
15	approve / approval	*no change*	○ □		○ □ ○
16	forget / forgettable	*no change*	○ □		○ □ ○ ○
17	telephone / telephonic	*moves from*	□ ○ ○	*to*	□ ○ □ ○
18	geriatrics / geriatrician	*moves from*	□ ○ □ ○	*to*	□ ○ ○ □ ○
19	edit / editor	*no change*	□ ○		□ ○ ○
20	picture / picturesque	*moves from*	□ ○	*to*	□ ○ □

Test 42

1 Nick Hornby's first novel, **High Fidelity**, was made into a successful film.
2 Westminster Abbey, **just opposite the Houses of Parliament,** is, **as you probably know,** where every Coronation takes place.
3 The Beatles – **John Lennon, Paul McCartney, George Harrison and Ringo Starr –** all came from Liverpool.
4 Jane Austen **(1775–1817)** was the author of a number of well-loved English novels.
5 Manchester United, **founded in 1902,** is the most successful of all British football clubs.
6 The US presidential election, **unfortunately,** was so close that it took several weeks before the winner was announced.
7 Leeds, **almost halfway between London and Edinburgh,** is a good place to break your journey north.
8 The Sydney Olympic Games, **it was generally felt,** were a great success.
9 Queen Elizabeth, **the elder daughter of King George VI,** married Philip in 1947.
10 Queen Elizabeth, **the elder daughter of King George VI,** married Philip, **son of Prince Andrew of Greece and created Duke of Edinburgh,** in 1947.

Test 43

1 I always like working *outdoors*. I'm really lucky to have found an *outdoor* job.
2 Put the TV on. We'll be just in time for the *ten o'clock* news.
3 As I novelist I'd say he is *first-rate*. But he's really a *second-rate* poet.
4 My friend's *Chinese* – she plays in a *Chinese* orchestra.
5 I live in *Piccadilly*, near *Piccadilly* Circus.
6 I really hate *over-cooked* vegetables.
7 They always wear really *up-to-date* clothes.
8 You can take a boat *upstream* from Greenwich to Westminster.
9 Your food will be *stone-cold* if you don't eat it now.
10 – Haven't you heard of her? She's a really *well-known* writer.
 – She can't be that *well-known* if I haven't heard of her.
11 He's a *good-looking* guy, but not as *good-looking* as he thinks he is.
12 Really *low-paid* workers find it difficult to buy new clothes.
13 I'll only ever eat *farm-fresh* eggs but I must admit that I often buy *oven-ready* chips.

Test 44

Check your pronunciation with the recording.

Test 45

1 £6.70 / $9.95
2 £6,229.84 / £23.97
3 £100 million (or £100 m) / 3p / 10p / 3,000 / 30,000
4 1.3L / 70,000 / £450
5 420 / 64MB (or 64Mb) / 10GB (or 10Gb) / 56K V90 / 98 / 15" (or 15-inch)
6 £11,000 / £16,400 / 5-day / 41-hour
7 020 8123 9999 / ED1 91A
8 M6 / 26 / M58 / 27 / 50 mph / 19 (or 19th) Sept
9 13–16°C / 55–61°F
10 Mon–Sat / 8pm / Thur, Sat / 3pm / 9 (or 9th) Dec / £10–£37.50
11 1749 / 1832
12 0.01% / 17,097.51 / 0.41% / HK$60 / 8.274 million (or 8.274 m) / 118%
13 0336 401 777 / 50p

Test 46

1 – Now ʷ I know you'd like a cup of tea.
   – No, ʷ I really fancy ʸ a coffee for a change.
2 – I'm not going to ʷ eat this!
   – Yes, you ʷ are! Have I ʸ ever made anything you didn't like?
3 Half the ʸ oranges I bought are bad, and I had to throw ʷ away ʸ all the ʸ apples!
4 Look, it's two ʷ o'clock now. Let's meet here at three ʸ o'clock.
5 My ʸ uncle Tom lives in Scotland, and my ʸ aunt Mary ʸ in Wales. They ʸ often meet up to go ʷ on holiday ʸ in Ireland together.
6 – Has she ʸ ever been to ʷ England?
   – No, ʷ I don't think she has. But she ʸ often goes to ʷ America.
7 – That was so ʷ interesting. I didn't know ʷ any of the ʸ actors, though. Did you?
   – I knew one or two ʷ of them.
8 Now ʷ I know you said you'd be ʸ a little late. But I've been waiting here two ʷ hours! More like two ʷ and a half, in fact!
9 I'd like to return this toy ʸ I bought from you last week.

Test 47

1 Several‿ of the speakers‿ are from‿ Africa, and one‿ or two from‿ America.
2 Tom's not‿ as‿ tall‿ as the rest‿ of the family.
3 We'll be there‿ at ten‿ o'clock,‿ if we're‿ at‿ all lucky.
4 My mother lives‿ in the USA and my mother‿ -in-law lives‿ in‿ England.
5 – Where's‿ Ann?
   – I've just left‿ (h)er on‿ (h)er‿ own. (Note: the /h/ in *her* disappears in normal speech.)
6 Peter‿ and Tom must be over‿ in the canteen,‿ I think.
7 I'll be there‿ in half‿ an‿ hour,‿ if‿ I can.
8 My brother‿ and sister‿ are‿ over here for two and‿ a half weeks.
9 – Where's‿ Andrew?
   – I've just seen‿ (h)im buying some‿ oranges‿ and‿ apples‿ in the market. (Note: the /h/ in *him* disappears in normal speech.)

Test 48

They lay‿ in the warm‿ air next to the lagoon where the water had sunk‿ into the pits‿ and marks‿ made by previous‿ creatures going to drink. The hum‿ of‿ insect‿ wings filled the‿ air. Peter felt happier than he had‿ ever been. His mind filled with thoughts. He thought how nice‿ it‿ was the way Jahunda was so patient‿ and‿ encouraging – not like his‿ own mother who‿ always fussed‿ and bothered. Scientists were‿ always saying that dinosaurs had small brains, but they were wrong. Dinosaurs thought differently, that‿ was‿ all.

Jahunda's‿ always‿ aware‿ of‿ everything around, he said to himself. She senses things. She smells‿ into the direction‿ of the wind‿ as‿ if the smells were visible. [....] [She] can measure with her body; she can lift‿ up‿ a great big‿ leg delicately to scratch‿ in‿ an‿ exact spot behind her head. She saves her massive‿ energy for when she needs‿ it‿ and doesn't crash‿ about‿ all the time roaring like‿ in the films. And dinosaur tails‿ are‿ always made to look so stiff‿ inside museums, when really they can move quite‿ well. Jahunda's‿ tail goes‿ on for‿ a long way behind her, but because‿ it's thick and strong at the base‿ and slender‿ at the tip, she can curve‿ it‿ up‿ and flick‿ large flies from her body so‿ expertly that they sail through the‿ air stone-dead.

As‿ if to‿ illustrate‿ his thoughts, Jahunda diverted the line‿ of white‿ ants which was marching single-file‿ across‿ her body with the touch‿ of‿ her tail, then gave‿ herself‿ a rasping scratch with‿ a toe where they‿ had been.

Test 49

1. an old aunt
2. My old uncle's ... for Easter
3. an egg ... of olives
4. from Marble Arch ... East End
5. Ann an(d) Andrew ... from Ankara to Athens
6. Northern Ireland ... South Africa
7. to us ... left out ... new address
8. phone after eight
9. last week ... are off ... next week
10. cold rain ... of Africa
11. I often ... tie it up
12. too old ... go out
13. She's obviously unhappy ... at work
14. How often ... go out in the evenings
15. I always ... to eat
16. They often ... far out ... sea in
17. an ice cream next week
18. I've always ... sail off into ... blue and
19. Mary about ... she is ... seen her
20. Peter is ... seen him

Test 50

1

– White coffee with sugar, please.
– **Black** with sugar for me, please.
– Black wi**thout** sugar.
– **I'll** have mine **white** without sugar.
– **Tea** without sugar for me, please.

2
- OK, I'm paying. What would you like?
- That's kind of you. Steak and chips, please.
- **I'd** like steak and chips, **too**.
- **Chick**en and chips, please.
- Can I have a chicken **cu**rry?
- **I'd** prefer a **fish** curry.

3
- What kind of pullover are you looking for?
- Light blue, I think.
- You'd look better in **dark** blue, in **my** opinion.
- If I wanted something **dark**, I'd go for dark **green**.
- OK. A dark green pullover, then.
- I've changed my mind. I'd like a dark green **shirt**, in**stead**.

4
- I'd like an apple pie.
- I think **I'd** prefer a **che**rry pie.
- **I'd** like some cherry **tart**.
- I don't want anything sweet. I'll have a cheese roll.
- And **I'll** have a cheese **sand**wich.
- I've changed my mind. **I'll** have a cheese sandwich, **too**.

5
- I'm going to Oxford next week.
- Oh, **I** went to Oxford **last** week.
- What a coincidence. **I** went there last week **too**.
- I went to **Cam**bridge last week.
- **I'm** going there **next** week.

Test 51
1 polite and friendly	5 polite and friendly
2 polite and friendly	6 polite and friendly
3 not very friendly	7 polite and friendly
4 not very friendly	8 not very friendly

Test 52
1 more could be said	5 more could be said
2 more could be said	6 more could be said
3 message complete	7 message complete
4 message complete	8 more could be said

Test 53

A

a *backpack* (a rucksack; piece of luggage worn on the back)
a *bandstand* (a platform for musicians, especially outdoors)
chit-chat (casual conversation about unimportant matters)
chock-a-block (completely full: *The train was chock-a-block*)
ding dong (the sound a bell makes: compare *tick tock*)
doom and gloom (pessimistic talk; a bad situation)
fight or flight (the choice, when in the face of danger)
a *fly-by* (an exhibition of aircraft, flying past at a special event)
hale and hearty (in excellent health)
helter-skelter (in hurry and confusion)

heyday (one's time of greatest success or fame)
higgledy-piggledy (all mixed up together, especially of small objects)
hip-hop (a type of dance and the music which accompanies it)
the *hoi polloi* (a condescending way to refer to 'ordinary' people)
a *hoo-ha* (a great commotion)
a *hurdy gurdy* (an old-fashioned stringed instrument with a handle)
a *hurly-burly* (a great commotion)
a *knick-knack* (a small ornament, usually of little value)
like it or lump it (accept it, whether you like it or not)
a *mishmash* (a confused mixture)
namby-pamby (weak and feeble)
pell-mell (hurrying in a confused or disorderly manner)
a *picnic* (an outdoor meal away from home)
ping pong (table tennis)
pitter-patter (the sound of light rain falling)
riff-raff (a negative term for undesirable people)
a *seesaw* (a plank balanced in the middle: playground equipment)
shipshape (tidy and well-organised)
teeny weeny (very small: a child's word)
tick tock (the sound a clock makes; compare *ding dong*)
tiptop (absolutely excellent)
a *titbit* (a nice little thing to eat *or* a small item of interesting news)
willy-nilly (whether you like it or not)

B

a) chock-a-block / knick-knacks
b) chit-chat
c) higgledy-piggledy
d) willy-nilly
e) heyday
f) doom and gloom
g) hale and hearty

Test 54

Horizontal
Jack, Fanny (*an old-fashioned name*), Annie/Anny, Anthony, Nina, Ken, Richard, Sally, Tessa, Tommy, Tina, Jake, Veronica
Vertical
Janice, Anna, Felicity, Ann/Anne, Angela, Norma, Norman, Eddy, Ruth, Paul, Ed
Diagonal
Wayne, Jane, Nick, Sophie, Mick, Kim, Dave, Kate

'Nicholas' is not in the maze: the first vowel is wrong.

Test 55

1 (k) cut-price	9 (h) excellent markets
2 (f) went bust	10 (j) architecture's nice
3 (g) wonderful place	11 (n) marvellous
4 (i) go in the sea	12 (o) even better
5 (c) stony	13 (a) sort of person
6 (d) brown soup	14 (p) breeze
7 (l) fantastically	15 (e) moving
8 (m) they've got it	16 (b) rain

Test 56

Across
1 cream / kriːm
4 desks / desks
8 tennis / tenɪs
9 low / ləʊ
10 it / ɪt
11 heel *or* heal / hiːl
12 singer / sɪŋə
13 I'm / aɪm
15 neater / niːtə
16 allows / əlaʊz
20 sit / sɪt
21 business / bɪznəs *or* bɪznɪs
24 support / səpɔːt
25 east / iːst
26 loud / laʊd

Down
1 Christmas / krɪsməs
2 eating / iːtɪŋ
3 metals / metəlz
4 divine / dɪvaɪn
5 'S' / es
6 cleaner / kliːnə
7 sole *or* soul / səʊl
14 meals / miːlz
17 lists / lɪsts
18 outer / aʊtə
19 asleep / əsliːp
21 bought / bɔːt
22 it / ɪt
23 nailed / neɪld

Test 57

1 aunts / dance
2 sense / fence
3 son / run

4 phone / loan
5 polite / fight

Test 58

Check your pronunciation with the recording.

Test 59

1a, 2b, 3b, 4a, 5b, 6b, 7b, 8b, 9a, 10a

Test 60

A

1d, 2i, 3f, 4g, 5j, 6a, 7e, 8b, 9c, 10h

B

1 (Q) What's your name?
2 (Q) Where do you come from?
3 (Q) Fancy a coffee?
4 (Q) (Are) you off now?
5 (Q) (Have you) got the time?

(R) Forgotten already?
(R) From Italy. And you?
(R) Not just now, thanks.
(R) Hold on a sec(ond).
(R) Ten past two.